STRATHCLYDE UNIVERSITY LIBRARY

30125 00089262 9

DIY robotics and sensors

with the BBC computer

practical projects for control applications

john billingsley

D1614762

UNIVERSITY OF
STRATHCLYDE LIBRARIES

05980/23

First published 1983 by:
Sunshine Books (an imprint of Scot Press Ltd.)
12–13 Little Newport Street,
London WC2R 3LD

Copyright © John Billingsley

ISBN 0 946408 13 0

All rights reserved. No part of this publication may be reproduced, stored in a retrieval system, or transmitted in any form or by any means, electronic, mechanical, photocopying, recording and/or otherwise, without the prior written permission of the Publishers.

Cover design by Graphic Design Ltd.
Illustration by Stuart Hughes.
Typeset and printed in England by Commercial Colour Press, London E7.

2

D
629.892
BIL

CONTENTS

Contents in detail

CHAPTER 7
A Simple Turtle
Mechanical design, control strategies and software.

CHAPTER 8
Interfacing a Robot
Building the robot language, teach mode, robot anatomy, six-axis control circuit.

CHAPTER 9
Analogue Ouput and Position Servos
Feedback and stability, circuits, analog output from CB2 with interrupts, driving radio-control servos.

CHAPTER 10
Simple Robot Vision
Adding a vision system to a robot, circuit, edge-following strategy, program for faster scan to screen.

CHAPTER 11
Whatever Next?
Robot evolution, intelligence, robot ping-pong contest.

CHAPTER 1
Getting Started

As the proud possessor of a BBC microcomputer, you have more computing power at your disposal than served the whole of Cambridge University in 1957. You have no doubt played endless games, written programs of your own and explored many of the mysteries of the machine itself. Now what?

Until now your machine has been dependent on keyed inputs for its performance — numbers on which to perform calculations or keystrokes to control games manoeuvres. Why not now let it get its own data? Why not add a muscle or two in the form of motors and relays, so that it can respond to the outside world? A new world of possibilities opens up, starting with turtles and robots, ending only at the bounds of imagination.

The simplest sensor channel uses one of the four analogue-to-digital convertor ports of the Model B. Even on the Model A, however, it is possible to measure an input voltage with no more than a resistor, a capacitor and the use of one bit of the user port — plus some cunning machine-code. Switches are simple to sense, and solid-state relays are little problem. Only when you want a variable output voltage do you have to consider adding more than a resistor or two — and even here it is possible to 'cheat' and obtain 256 output levels with just two more resistors and another capacitor.

A lot can be achieved without a very deep technical knowledge of computer architecture, although I hope that you will learn about the fundamentals as you work through the book. As any new term is introduced it is put in quotes, and an attempt made to explain it. Now and again quotes may be used for a 'buzz word', for which an explanation is not really necessary.

The first few chapters may seem very simple and obvious. Often, however, it is the most trivial point, such as 'which way up does the connector go' which will catch you in the back of the neck. The robot chapter may seem rather specific to one brand of robot. In fact it addresses the general problem of commanding a multitude of channels through a limited user port.

As each chapter was written, the designs and programs were tried and tested, and for this I am very grateful for the collaboration of Timothy

Dadd. Anything which has reached print should have worked at least once! Good luck.

Basic equipment

The components required for the construction of interfaces and systems are described in each chapter. In addition you will need a small soldering iron and some multicore solder. Reliable soldering is an art which can take years to perfect. One essential is to 'tin' both wires to be joined by melting fresh solder against each one separately. Never carry a blob of molten solder on the iron — in just a few seconds it can form a crust which will disguise a 'dry joint' and cause hours of troubleshooting.

You will also need a test meter. Buy a simple moving-coil multimeter, not a digital meter. You will be more interested in the rough value of a signal, whether it is ground or logic high, rather than its value to three places of decimals. Moreover it is more convincing to see a needle move, requiring tens of microamps, than to see digits flicker which can be influenced by a small charge of static. The purpose of the meter is to eliminate uncertainty when something unexpected is happening, and it is little help if you must first wonder if the meter is showing a true story.

Although an attempt has been made to detail the components down to the last piece of wire, some extra wire will certainly come in useful — a metre or two of every colour you can find. Single strand 0.6mm equipment wire will probably be easiest to use.

Construction methods

You will note on flicking through the pages that there is not a printed circuit in sight. When you have developed and proved a device, be it turtle or simple smoothing circuit, you may wish to construct a permanent version of the circuitry laid out with great neatness. However this book is not concerned with knitting patterns. Instead it tries to establish the principles of interfacing gadgetry to a computer with a minimum of fuss. A three-dimensional rat's nest of components hanging on a connector strip may look untidy, but if carefully soldered the chances of error can be slight. Start with a lash-up which works, and only then transfer it to a more elegant form. Then when you find that the circuit no longer works, you will look for dry joints, hairline cracks in the printed circuit tracks, or whiskers of copper bridging tracks which you thought you had cut.

Power supply unit

Some of the later designs call for a power supply capable of driving small motors. Although the BBC micro has some spare power capacity, it is much less risky to use a separate supply.

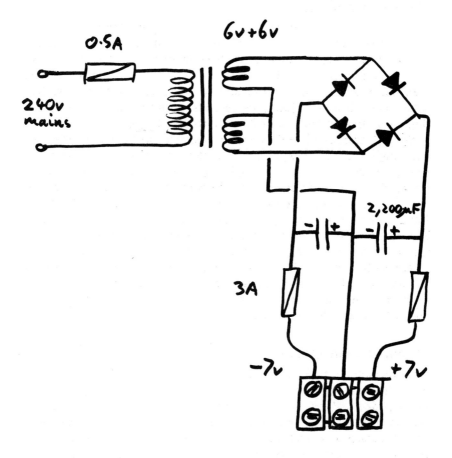

Figure 1.1   Simple power supply
*Transformer available from RS (no 207–245). Diode bridge
(no 262–113)*

The components consist of a transformer with two 6v outputs, a diode bridge and two reservoir capacitors. This will give outputs of $+7v$ and $-7v$, which can alternatively be used as a single 14v supply. You will also need mains cable, at least one and preferably three fuses, three screw terminals or three ways of connector strip, and a suitable box to mount it all in.

A 50 VA transformer will give plenty of margin against overload; the RS 207 – 245 should cost no more than five pounds. A suitable 4 amp diode bridge is the RS 262 – 113 costing a pound or so, whilst 2,200 microfarad 16v RS 103 – 373 capacitors are about fifty pence each. For the applications here there is no need to smooth the supplies, but a single-package stabiliser can easily be added later. The mains supply should be fused at 0.5 amp, and there should preferably be 3 amp fuses in the outputs.

CHAPTER 2
It goes in here

The computer thrives on a diet of numbers, stored in memory as binary digits or 'bits', and manipulated by the processor to form results which are also numbers. Within the computer electrical signals are either close to 5v, representing a logic 'one', or are close to ground (0v) and represent 'zero'. From combinations of such signals the numerical values are built up in the scale of two; one eight-bit byte can represent numbers from 0 to 255, two taken together can be interpreted as numbers from 0 to 65535, or alternatively from -32768 to $+32767$.

The outside world is not often like that. Keys on the keyboard do take binary values, either 'pressed' or 'not pressed', but other quantities such as positions of robots, speeds of motors or voltages on control knobs can vary continuously over their range. Somehow these 'analogue' values must be turned into numbers, so that the computer can digest them.

In this chapter you will meet the interface already built into the Model B which allows you to connect up to four analogue signals such as potentiometer voltages or any other voltage in the range 0 to 2.5 volts. You can build a simple cable and connector strip which will come in useful time and time again for trying out input schemes with a minimum of effort, and can add a joystick which will enable you to drive the graphics program of the next chapter. You will also find how to add a 'light-pen' to your computer, enabling you to select an item from the screen simply by pointing at it.

A connector for the analogue port

The Model B is equipped with a connector providing four analogue inputs, together with a 5v supply. I suspect that this was designed expressly for the connection of a pair of joysticks for games purposes — indeed two bits of logic input (bits PB0 and PBI of a 'private' VIA) also appear on the connector for 'zapping' buttons. Also there is a light-pen connection which certainly merits later investigation.

A good confidence-builder is the construction and use of a home-grown joystick. Later this can be regarded as a simple piece of test equipment to trouble-shoot analogue inputs in general. Even with a device as simple as this, containing only two potentiometers, the chances of non-working are

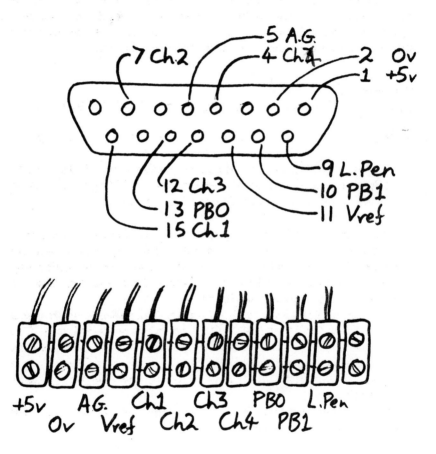

Figure 2.1   Analogue port connections

legion. The important thing is to proceed step by step, eliminating uncertainty as you go.

First make up a connector to the analogue socket. You will need a 15-pin D-type male plug such as Farnell 140–822 or RS 466–185, a 12-way length of 'chocolate block' connector strip and enough wire to join them — either 60cm of ribbon cable or an equivalent assortment of coloured wires. In this way, the connections will be brought to a convenient point near the keyboard so that you can trouble-shoot hardware and software together.

It is worth 'unscrambling' the pins, so that the signals on the connector strip are in a sensible order. The wiring order then becomes:

Connector strip:

Signal:	+5v	0v	A.G	Vref	Ch.1	Ch.2	Ch.3	Ch.4	PB0	PB1	LPen
Plug:											
Pin No.	1	2	5	11	15	7	12	4	13	10	9

Note: In the BBC Manual, the analogue input pins are labelled CH0 to CH3. Since the values are read by the functions ADVAL(1) to ADVAL(4) it makes more sense to think of them as Ch.1 to Ch.4.

After wiring the connector strip, plug it in and check it. The secret of successful electronic development is not to trust *anything*. If you are convinced that there is a signal at one end of a wire, *check* that it really appears at the other — otherwise your faith in the wire and its soldering may cost you hours of searching for a bug.

First use a simple multimeter (6v DC range, — ve to the 0v line) to check out the + 5v and Vref connections. Vref will appear as about 2 volts. Also check PB0 and PB1, which will be between 4 and 5v. The use of a simple needle-and-scale meter does much more to inspire confidence than a flickering reading on a digital meter, especially when inspecting signals which are changing.

Now it is time to check the analogue input connections. Enter the following program into the micro:


```
10  PRINT ADVAL(1),ADVAL(2),ADVAL(3),ADVAL(4)
20  GOTO 10
```


and run it. The screen should fill with four columns of values of (or near) zero. Now connect a wire to Vref, and touch the end onto each of Ch.1 to Ch.4 in turn. You will see the appropriate column of the screen change to the value of 65520 (or thereabouts) as each channel is touched — your confidence is growing.

Finally check out PB0 and PB1. (Note that these are *not* the same PB0 and PB1 which you will meet later on the user port.) Enter the program:

```
10 PRINT ADVAL(0) AND 3
20 GOTO 10
```

Remove the test wire from Vref and connect it instead to 0v. While the program is running, touch the wire to PB0 and PB1 in turn. The values 1 and 2 should appear respectively.

Constructing a joystick

Now how about the joystick. For this you will need two potentiometers of value 100 kilohms. RS 161–818 would be suitable, but almost anything goes. Even the resistance value is not particularly critical, and provided not more than two potentiometers are to be driven from Vref a value as low as 10k will do no harm. Start simply. The potentiometer consists of a resistive track, connected to the outer solder tags. The middle solder tag is connected to the 'wiper', which slides along the track as the shaft is rotated and picks off an intermediate voltage corresponding to its position. Connect the outer tags of one potentiometer to Analogue Ground (A.G) and Vref respectively. Connect the middle tag to Ch.1, then enter and run the first of the programs above. As you rotate the shaft to and fro, you will see the numbers in the first column vary from 0 to 65520.

They didn't? Then check the voltage on the potentiometer wiper using the multimeter. None there? Then take out the potentiometer and measure its resistance, and the resistance between the wiper and each end as the knob is rotated. Looks OK? Then put it back and try again, check the value of Vref. All looks OK, but still no changing numbers? Then check out Ch.1 again as above, go to bed, try again in the morning.

Now connect the second potentiometer outer tags also to Analogue Ground and Vref, and its wiper to Ch.2. Now when the test program is run, you should be able to control the numbers in both columns one and two. Your electronic problems are at an end, and you are faced wth the task of combining the mechanical movements into that of a joystick. One possibility is sketched in **Figure 2.2**.

If all else fails, a commercial joystick can be bought for under ten pounds — you might even prefer to buy an obsolete TV game and murder it to obtain a pair of joysticks.

So far, this chapter must have been most frustrating for owners of a Model A. Even though the Model A has no analogue input ports, it is still

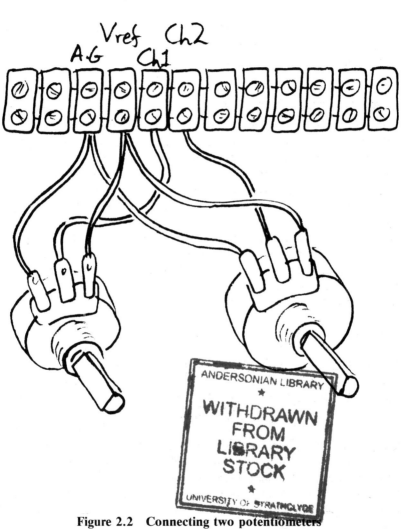

Figure 2.2   Connecting two potentiometers

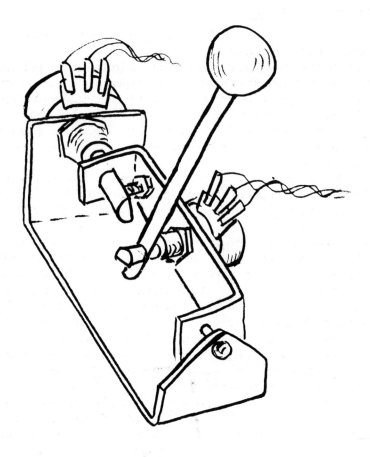

Figure 2.3   A simple joystick

possible to attach a joystick — using a certain amount of skulduggery as described in Chapter 5. Before that can be done, it is necessary to understand the machinations of the user port, and the intricacies of the Versatile Interface Adaptor or VIA.

Adding a light-pen

Before we move on, remember that tempting light-pen connection? What is a light-pen, and what can it do?

The television display is, of course, built up from a single spot which scans across the picture fifteen thousand times per second, working from top to bottom fifty times per second. If a pen containing a phototransistor is held against the screen, then as the spot passes beneath it the phototransistor will give a pulse of output current. From the timing of this pulse it is possible to work out the position of the point on the screen which is being selected.

With the right interface, it should be possible to put up a set of options on the screen — perhaps 'up', 'down', 'left', 'right' for robot commands — and to select an option merely by pointing to the word on the screen with a pen connected by a wire to the computer.

The 'official' light-pen interface is an enormous box of tricks, and is not particularly cheap. The reason for its complexity is that it tries to resolve the pen position to a single 'pixel' or picture spot — a single letter is made up of 64 pixels, arranged 8 by 8. Can you get away with anything simpler? Provided you only want to resolve to one character in mode 7, a circuit consisting of one phototransistor OP500, one 10 kilohm resistor and an NPN transistor 2N3705 is all you need — total cost under one pound!

The light-pen connection leads to a 6845 CRT controller chip. This is an industrious device which turns a collection of numbers in memory into an appropriate picture on the screen. Suppose that the first line of text to appear on the screen is 'the quick brown fox'. The chip first looks at the memory location to be represented at the start of the line — here it holds the code for the letter 't'. From a special memory it must now look up the shape of the letter 't', or especially it must look up the pattern for the top scan-line of the 't'. As this is being used to modulate the tube's electron beam, the chip picks up the code for 'h' and looks up the pattern for its top line, and so on to the end of the row of letters. When the scan line is complete, the chip looks at the 't' a second time, now looking up the pattern for its second line, and so on until eight scan lines have been output. The address of the letter being processed is held in a sixteen-bit register within the chip, and this is automatically incremented to follow the text down the page.

Whenever the light-pen pin changes from logic level 0 to 1, the address of the character being displayed at that instant is snapped by the two 8-bit

17

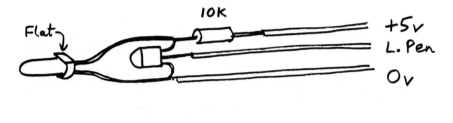

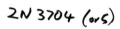

2N 3704 (or 5)

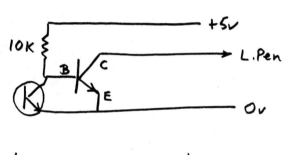

Photo-
transistor

NPN transistor.

Figure 2.4   Light pen

registers within the chip. From their value, it is possible to work out where the character appeared on the screen, and hence react appropriately. The chip is one of those awkward ones which try to conserve addressing space (see Chapter 4) by having to be prodded with the register number at one address, and parting with the answer at a second. Don't worry too much if the following program seems to be mumbo jumbo, it's short and it works:

```
10 REM SIMPLE LIGHT-PEN DEMO
20 MODE 7: SCTOP = 10245: REM NEAR SCREEN-TOP
ADDRESS
30 X = 0:Y = 0 :REM COORDINATES FOR LIGHT-PEN 'HIT'
40 BLK$ = CHR$(32) :REM BLACK BLOB
50 WHT$ = CHR$(255):REM WHITE BLOB
60 FOR I = 1 TO 999
70 VDU 255:NEXT: REM FILL SCREEN WITH WHITE
```

Here comes the mumbo jumbo:

```
80 CRTC = &FE00 : REM ADDRESS OF CRT CHIP

100 ?CRTC = 17:A = ?(CRTC + 1): REM READ REGISTERS 17
110 ?CRTC = 16:A = ?(CRTC + 1) + 256*A:REM AND 16
120 A = A − SCTOP: REM A IS NOW CHARACTER NUMBER
ON SCREEN
130 IF A< 0 OR A> 999 THEN 100 :REM MISSED!
```

Now let's use the result to move a screen blob:

```
140 PRINT TAB(X,Y) WHT$;: REM RUB OUT OLD BLOB
150 X = A MOD 40: Y = A DIV 40: REM BREAK A INTO X,Y
160 PRINT TAB(X,Y) BLK$: REM BLACK BLOB AT HIT
170 GOTO 100: REM AND DO IT AGAIN
```

This is a good simple program to convince you that the technique works. However Tim Dadd felt that you would like something more entertaining. Below is his answer to the Stylophone. Doh, Re, Mi etc. will appear on the screen, with a column of blobs to the left. Point the light pen at a note, and that note will start to play; the column to the left gives blessed silence. Have pity on the neighbours.

Moving Blob

```
 10 REM LIGHT PEN DEMO FOR MODE 7
 20 MODE 7
 30 SCREENTOP=10245
 40 VDU23,1;0;0;0 :REM TURN OFF CURSOR
 50 X=0:Y=0
 60 BLK$=CHR$32 :REM SPACE=BLACK
 70 WHT$=CHR$255 :REM 255=WHITE SQUARE
 80 FOR I=0 TO 1000 :REM PAINT SCREEN
 90    PRINT WHT$; :REM WHITE PAINT
100    NEXT
110 CRTC=&FE00 :REM CRT CONTROL 6845
120 ?CRTC=17:A=?(CRTC+1)
130 ?CRTC=16:A=?(CRTC+1)*256+A
140 A=A-SCREENTOP :REM MAKE 0-999
150 IF A>998 OR A<0 THEN 120
160 PRINT TAB(X,Y)WHT$; :REM REPAINT
170 X=A MOD40:Y=A DIV40
180 PRINT TAB(X,Y)BLK$; :REM BLACKEN
190 GOTO120 :REM AND AGAIN
```

Tim's Music Program

```
 10 REM LIGHT PEN DEMO FOR MODE 7
 20 MODE 7
 30 SCREENTOP=10245
 40 VDU23,1;0;0;0 :REM CURSOR OFF
 50 X=0:Y=0
 51 WHT$=CHR$255 :REM 255=WHITE SQUARE
 52 PITCH=98
 60 FOR I=0 TO 12:READ N$
 61    PRINT TAB(20-(RIGHT$(N$,1)="#")*3,I*
2)WHT$;N$;TAB(17,I*2-1)WHT$;
 62    NEXT
110 CRTC=&FE00 :REM CRT CONTROL 6845
120 ?CRTC=17:A=?(CRTC+1)
130 ?CRTC=16:A=?(CRTC+1)*256+A
140 A=A-SCREENTOP :REM MAKE 0-999
150 IF A>998 OR A<0 THEN 120
170 Y=A DIV40
180 P=PITCH-2*Y
190 IF P AND2 THEN SOUND1,-10,P,1
```

```
 200 GOTO120
1000 DATA DOH,TI,LA#,LA,SOH#,SOH
1010 DATA FA#,FA,MI,RE#,RE,DOH#,DOH
```

CHAPTER 3
Graphic Design with a Joystick

I am married to a graphic designer. One day Ros wanted to find out more about computer graphics, and to design some screen displays. The program described in this chapter was 'run up' to let her explore some of the possibilities. It makes a good excuse to use a joystick, and even includes a touch of digital filtering to remove the joystick's jitter.

Program specification

The functions which the program provides are Point, Line, Fill, Centre and Shape, whilst the colour is set by pressing a number between 1 and 8. As the joystick is moved, a fleeting dot moves about the screen. Pressing P marks a fixed dot onto the screen, and also memorises the coordinates of the point in an array of 'last four points'.

If the joystick is moved and L is pressed, a line is drawn from the last recorded point. Another move and another L draws a second line from the end of the first, and so on. If the L key is held down, line segments will be drawn in swift succession, forming a smooth curve drawn by the joystick movement.

Record a point with P, move the joystick, record a second point, move the joystick again and press F. The triangle defined by the points will be Filled in with solid colour.

Holding down F and moving the joystick does not produce a satisfactory effect; the result is just a rather fat line, as each set of three points along the trail is filled. If you wish to fill a shape you must first define a centre within it — move the joystick and press C. Now each time you press S, the triangle formed by the centre, the present point and the previous point will be filled in. Holding S you can draw and fill any shape surrounding the centre, provided the radius does not try to 'double back'. By a nimble redefinition of the centre, you can draw shapes as convoluted as you wish.

To avoid accidentally erasing the work of art, the clear command is an exclamation mark, requiring you to hold 'shift' at the same time.

At any stage a number key can be pressed to define a new colour.

The joystick routine

That, then, is the specification of the program. How do we set about writing it? A good starting point is the joystick routine itself. This must use ADVAL commands to read the two analogue voltages, and then translate them into movements on the screen in the range 0 to 1200 for X and 0 to 1000 for Y. There must then be a dot shown in the selected position, which must be removed when the joystick is moved to a new place. The dot must contrast with the background, whatever the colour. This means that we must first measure the colour of the screen at the joystick position with POINT(X,Y), remember the value in variable OC (old colour) and plant a spot of colour 7-OC, using PLOT 69,X,Y. Before reading a new joystick value the old value must be put back and round we go again.

```
1000  DEF PROCJOY
1010  GCOL 0,C:PLOT 69,X,Y: REM PUT BACK OLD
COLOUR
1020  X = ADVAL(1)/SCALE: REM SCALE DEPENDS ON
SENSITIVITY
1030  Y = LIM − ADVAL(2)/SCALE: REM LIM = 1000, Y,
INVERTED
1040  OC = POINT(X,Y):GCOL 0,7-OC:PLOT 69,X,Y:REM PUT
DOT
1050  ENDPROC
```

The choice between ADVAL(n)/SCALE and LIM − ADVAL(n)/SCALE depends on the potentiometer connections. If the voltage increases in the positive X or Y direction, the first form is used. A 'genuine' BBC joystick gives positive X and negative Y, hence the combination here. With a home-made joystick, the X and Y scales may need to be different. The movement of the joystick may only rotate each potentiometer shaft over a fraction of its range, and each channel may need to have an offset LIMX, LIMY added, fiddled in value to make the centre of the screen coincide with joystick centre. Lines 1020, 1030 might then appear as:

```
1020  X = ADVAL(1)/SCS + LIMX
1030  Y = LIMY − ADVAL(2)/SCY
```

and inserting a temporary line to print X and Y could help in choosing the values of LIMX, LIMY, SCX and SCY.

When you come to try the program, you will probably find that the selected spot is subject to a certain amount of jitter. It is easy to include digital filtering in the program to reduce this. Consider first the simple instruction:

$$X = ADVAL(1)$$

As soon as the analogue value changes, the value of X will change to match it. Now consider instead:

$$X = X + (ADVAL(1) - X)/2$$

If the ADVAL value has been zero for a while, and suddenly changes to 1000, then the next value of X will be $0 + (1000 - 0)/2 = 500$. The following value will be $500 + (1000 - 500) = 750$, and so on. Each time through the program the difference between X and the ADVAL value will halve so that X will eventually catch up with ADVAL, although the effect of sudden changes will be smoothed out. Using a number bigger than 2 in the program line will give more smoothing, but X will take longer to catch up with the ADVAL. This smoothing system is called a 'low pass filter'. It gives the same effect that would be gained by putting a series resistor and shunt capacitor into the analogue circuit. If the program line is made:

$$X = X + (ADVAL(1) - X)/F$$

the value of F can be chosen to give a variety of time-constants. The longer the time-constant, the less effect jitter noise will have, but the slower will be the response of the joystick.

Now if filtering is desired, lines 1020 and 1030 can be replaced by

```
1020 X = X + (ADVAL(1)/SCALE - X)/F
1030 Y = Y + (LIM - ADVAL(2)/SCALE - Y)/F
```

The rest of the program

Now let us deal with the housekeeping. There is so little that it might as well remain at the start:

```
  10 MODE 2:VDU 5:REM GRAPHICS WITH SEVEN STEADY
COLOURS
  20 COM$ = "PLFCS!":REM STRING OF COMMAND
LETTERS
  30 DIM X(3),Y(3):REM STORE FOR LAST THREE POINTS
  40 SCALE = 30:LIM = 1000:F = 2
  50 COL = 7:OC = 0:X = − 1:Y = − 1:XC = 50:YC = 500:N = 0
```

Now we can start the main loop:

First read the joystick, showing its position as a dot, then display a line of the selected colour in the bottom left of the screen:

```
 100 PROCJOY
 110 MOVE 0,0:GCOL 0,COL:COLOUR COL:VDU 255
```

Next test for a key-press. If none, loop via joystick test.

```
 120 A$ = INKEY$ 5:IFA$ = ""THEN 100
```

Is the key a number? If so, change colour and loop:

```
 130 A = VAL(A$):IF  A>0  THEN  COL = (A − 1)AND  7:
GOTO 100
```

Which of the commands is A$? If none, loop.

```
 140 A = INSTR(COM$,A$):IF A = 0 THEN 100
```

If the command is 'point', use a special route:

```
 150 IF A = 1 THEN GOSUB 190:GOTO100
```

Otherwise rub out the dot, set up the colour, call the selected routine, note the new dot colour and loop again:

```
160 GCOL 0,OC:PLOT 69,X,Y:GCOL 0,COL
170 GOSUB A*100:OC = POINT(X,Y):GOTO100
```

Now the 'point' subroutine notes X,Y in the 'circular' array, and reverses OC so that a permanent dot will be left.

```
190 N = (N + 1)AND3:X(N) = X:Y(N) = Y:OC = 7 – OC:RETURN
```

The 'line' subroutine notes the new end point, then draws a line from the previous point:

```
200 GOSUB 190:M = (N – 1)AND3:GCOL 0,COL
210 MOVE X(M),Y(M):DRAW X(N),Y(N):RETURN
```

The 'fill' routine first flushes the PLOT routine's point memory, then calls PLOT 85 with the coordinates of the latest three points to fill a triangle:

```
300 GOSUB 190:FORI = 1 TO 3:MOVE X,Y:NEXT
310 FOR I = 0 TO 2:PLOT 85,X((N – I)AND3),
Y((N – I) AND 3):NEXT
320 RETURN
```

The 'centre' routine notes the centre, then flushes PLOT's memory as well as the local point memory:

```
400 GOSUB 190:XC = X:YC = Y
410 FOR I = 0 TO 3:MOVE X,Y:X(I) = X:Y(I) = Y:
NEXT:RETURN
```

Now 'shape' reads the latest point, and fills a triangle formed by the centre, the latest and the previous points:

```
500 GOSUB 190
510 FOR I = 0 TO 1:MOVE X((N – I)AND3),
Y((N – I) AND 3):NEXT
520 PLOT 85,XC,YC:RETURN
```

And finally there is the clear-screen routine:

```
600 COLOUR 128:GCOL 0,128:CLS:OC = 0:RETURN
```

Now you can let your artistic talents run wild. You will need a very steady hand to drive the joystick when holding down a key for continuous writing, and you should take care to let the stored-up keystrokes run out afterwards. The results can be most impressive — especially if you are married to a graphic designer.

Joystick Graphics

```
   10 MODE2:VDU 5:REM GAPHICS WITH SEVEN STE
ADY COLURS
   20 COM$="PLFCS!":REM STRING OF COMMAND LE
TTERS
   30 DIM X(3),Y(3):REM STORE FOR LAST THREE
   POINTS
   40 SCALE=30:LIM=1000:F=2
   50 COL=7:OC=0:X=-1:Y=-1:XC=500:YC=500:N=0
 100 PROCJOY
 110 MOVE0,0:GCOL 0,COL:COLOUR COL:VDU255
 120 A$=INKEY$ 5:IFA$=""THEN100
 130 A=VAL(A$):IF A>0 THEN COL=(A-1)AND 7:GO
TO 100
 140 A=INSTR(COM$,A$):IF A=0 THEN 100
 150 IF A=1 THEN GOSUB 190
 160 GCOL 0,OC:PLOT 69,X,Y:GCOL 0,COL
 170 GOSUB A*100:OC=POINT(X,Y):GOTO 100
 180 N=(N+1)AND3:X(N)=X:Y(N)=Y:OC=7-OC:RETURN
 190 N=(N+1)AND3:X(N)=X:Y(N)=Y:OC=7-OC:RETURN
 200 GOSUB 190:M=(N-1)AND3:GCOL 0,COL
 210 MOVE X(M),Y(M):DRAW X(N),Y(N):RETURN
 300 GOSUB 190:FORI=1 TO 3:MOVE X,Y:NEXT
 310 FOR I=0 TO 2:PLOT 85,X((N-I)AND3),Y((N-
I)AND3):NEXT
 320 RETURN
 400 GOSUB 190:XC=X:YC=Y
 410 FOR I=0 TO 3:MOVE X,Y:X(I)=X:Y(I)=Y:NEX
T:RETURN
```

```
 500 GOSUB 190
 510 FOR I=0 TO 1:MOVE X((N-I)AND3),Y((N-I)
AND3):NEXT
 520 PLOT 85,XC,YC:RETURN
 600 COLOUR 128:GCOL 0,128:CLS:OC=0:RETURN
1000 DEF PROCJOY
1010 GCOL 0,OC:PLOT 69,X,Y: REM PUT BACK OLD
COLOUR
1020 X=ADVAL(1)/SCALE: REM SCALE DEPENDS ON
SENSITIVITY
1030 Y=LIM-ADVAL(2)/SCALE :REM LIM=1000, Y
INVERTED
1040 OC=POINT(X,Y):GCOL0,7-OC:PLOT 69,X,Y:R
EM PUT DOT
1050 ENDPROC
```

CHAPTER 4
It comes out there

In Chapter 2, some mention was made about the internal goings-on of the computer and the difference between analogue and digital signals. Even when the external signals are digital, bringing them to the computer's attention is not altogether an easy matter.

Digital interfaces

The spine of the microcomputer is made up of two 'buses', bunches of signals which connect most of the components together. The simplest of these is the data bus. When the processor (another name for the microprocessor chip) wants to store a data byte in memory, it switches the corresponding logic voltages onto the eight-bit data bus, issues a command, and the appropriate memory location remembers the data. When the processor wants to retrieve a byte, whether of data or the next instruction in its program, it sends its command and the memory applies the logic voltages to the data bus for the processor to read. You will see that the data bus is extremely busy, and an attempt to apply external signals to it could well send the processor diving in a spin.

To order the memory about, the processor must be able to specify an address. Now we find the second bus, the sixteen-bit address bus. 65,536 different addresses can be specified as the bus stands, but a little cheating can extend it to address any size of memory you can afford. Another important line allows the processor to tell the memory whether it wants to read or write data.

What has all this to do with interfacing? Clearly something has to be placed between any logic input line and the data bus, so that the data is only allowed onto the bus for the brief instant when the processor wants to read it. This is the role of the interface chip. It means, for instance, that eight pins of 'port B' can be connected to a plug on the machine for the convenience of the user. Slip a socket onto this connector, and you can attach extra keys, sensor contacts, or any other sort of logic signal, and with a program command or two read them into the computer. This then is the user port.

Notched teeth
cut into insulation
and make contact

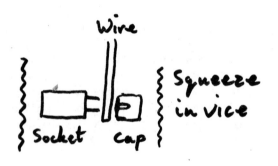

Wire

Socket   Cap

Squeeze
in vice

Fold cable over back
and squeeze on
metal clip.

Figure 4.1   Connector (with cable clip)
(Connector with cable ready attached can be brought from Acorn dealers)

Making connections to the user port

Before getting to grips with the user port, it is a good idea to bring it within reach. This entails making a connecting cable similar to the one described in Chapter 2 to bring the signals to a connector strip beside the keyboard. The connector in this case is a 20-way RS 467–289 socket, which is designed for use with ribbon cable RS 357–867 (costing about one pound per metre). With care, the cable can be joined to the connector socket using a vice. Chop off the end of the cable in a neat straight line (do not bare the wires). Slot the ribbon neatly into the slot in the socket top, and carefully assemble the 'business end' of the socket into the top until the sharp contact Vs just touch the cable. Make sure that the cable is square, so that each V straddles its own wire, then carefully squeeze the socket and top together in a vice so that each V cuts through the insulation and connects to its wire. Now bend the ribbon over the back of the socket and squeeze on the metal clip to hold everything in place.

Model A only

If your computer is a Model A, it may well lack a user port connector. Instead you can use an edge-connector of 0.1 inch pitch. This must be single- or separate-sided, ie must not connect the top tracks to the bottom. It must make contact to 12 tracks, with a 13th position blocked with a polarising key — this fits into the slot in the circuit board to ensure correct alignment. The business side of the board is the top — ie the keyboard side. Pin 1 is at the far end from the polarising slot. The edge connector actually starts at pin 0, with connections:

0	1	2	3	4	5	6	7	8	9	10	11	
+ 5v	CB1	CB2	PB0	PB1	PB2	PB3	PB4	PB5	PB6	PB7	0v	(slot)

The Model A might also lack chip 69, a 6522 VIA, since this is only used for the user and printer ports. The socket will be present, just in front of the 6502 processor chip, and you should have no trouble plugging in five pounds-worth of interface chip.

Chocolate block connections

If you have a Model B, or an A with an added connector, crimping the cable is only half the battle. You now need to unscramble the connections to the connector strip. Of the twenty wires, ten are connected to either 0 volts or 5 volts. These are alternate conductors, starting from pin 1. Wires 1 and 3 carry + 5v, and should carefully be connected to position 1 of the connector strip. Wires 5, 7, 9, 11, 13, 15, 17, 19 are all grounded; it is

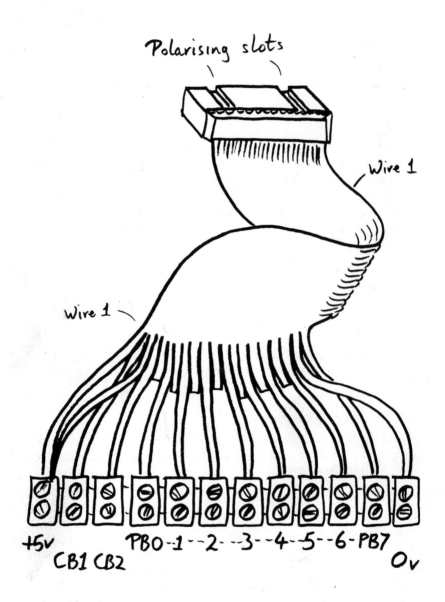

Figure 4.2   User port cable

probably best to connect wire 19 to connector strip position 12, and to cut the other grounds slightly short to keep them out of the way. Now wires 2, 4, 6, 8, 10, 12, 14, 16, 18 and 20 are joined to connector strip positions 2 to 11 respectively. This will give the following arrangement of signals on the connector strip:

(Wire):	1,3	2	4	6	8	10	12	14	16	18	20	19
Position:	1	2	3	4	5	6	7	8	9	10	11	12
Signal:	+5v	CB1	CB2	PB0	PB1	PB2	PB3	PB4	PB5	PB6	PB7	0v

After plugging the socket (or the edge connector) into the BBC micro, check out the signals using the multimeter. Connect the negative test lead to position 12. Check for +5v on position 1 — if it is not there, perhaps the socket is the wrong way round. Signals PB0 to PB7 can be checked by a mystic means which will become clear later in this chapter. Enter the program:

```
10 PRINT 255-?&FE60
20 GOTO 10
```

Run the program, and connect a wire from 0v in turn to PB0, PB1 up to PB7. The values 1, 2, 4, 8, 16, 32, 64 and 128 should appear on the screen respectively.

How the interface works

Now at last we are in a position to look at the operation of the user port. The signals which concern us at first are PB0 to PB7, which are taken from the B-port of a Versatile Interface Adaptor. The VIA is so versatile that it can baffle in an instant — the BBC Manual shies away from describing it after a single paragraph. It is a single chip, a 6522, memory-mapped to appear at address & FE60 (the & denotes hexadecimal). If this makes sense to you, skip the next few paragraphs.

Early computer systems used a special 'bus' system for controlling input/output, and many microcomputers still have special input and output instructions. It was soon realised, however, that inputs and outputs could be treated as though they were memory locations. When a number is saved in memory, say in location &1234, voltages are altered within the circuitry of one of the memory chips. If these were amplified and connected to the outside world, they could drive eight output lines, so that storing a value of zero would set all eight lines low, whilst 255 would set them all high. When the contents of a memory location are loaded on the other hand, the logic values of voltages stored in one of the chips will be copied into the accumulator of the microcomputer. Suppose that instead of stored voltages, these signals came from wires connected to eight voltages in the outside world, then we would have eight inputs. An interface chip can thus be designed which will have a lot in common with a memory chip — and some manufacturers produce chips which combine both functions.

Address decoding

The sixteen address lines of the 6502 microcomputer can directly address 65536 separate bytes of memory — many more than will fit on the average memory chip. The top few address bits are thus decoded to give lines to address individual memory chips, whilst the remaining bits are connected to all chips in parallel to determine the address within the selected chip. (Not absolutely true for some sorts of RAM, but ignore that for now). Not all the memory chips need to be present to make the system work, so there may be blank spaces within the 'memory map' of the machine.

If the top four lines are decoded, there will be sixteen 'chip-select' lines, the first responding to addresses from &0000 to &0FFF, the next from &1000 to &1FFF and so on. One of these, the &F line for instance, could enable another decoder to decode the next four lines, giving sixteen more signals which would respond to addresses &F0XX, &F1XX ..... &FFXX, where XX can be any two hex digits. One of these lines, say the one which responds to &FEXX, can enable yet another decoder giving a further sixteen lines which respond to &FE0X, &FE1X etc. Finally one of these lines, say the &FE6X line, could enable a chip with just 16 memory addresses, &FE60 to &FE6F. Now suppose that instead of being a genuine memory chip, this chip can be connected to the outside world. Then if we save the value 7 (binary 00000111) in address &FE60 we can control eight output lines to make three pins go high and another five go low. That in a nutshell (coconut?) is the principle of memory-mapped input-output. The trouble is that we now have to crack open the nut — and the 6522 is a hard nut to crack!

Ports and data direction

Sixteen bytes have 128 bits. If we had separate lines for inputs and outputs that would leave us with an awful lot of pins on the chip. After providing the signals required to connect the chip into the micro system (18 lines) plus two lines for power supply, a 40-pin pack does not have much to spare. The 20 remaining pins are arranged as two 'ports', each with eight data lines and two control or 'handshake' lines. It is one of these ports, PB0–7 with its control lines CB1 and CB2, which should by now be connected to the connector strip beside your keyboard. It may look like a connector to you, but the computer is convinced that it is the memory byte at the address &FE60. Each port is bidirectional, that is each individual bit can be an input or an output. The direction of each bit is held in a register within the chip called (wait for it) the Data Direction Register. For the user port, the computer addresses DDR-B at &FE62. Each bit which is made a 1 at this address will be selected as an output bit, whilst the 0s will select inputs.

Now how do we go about looking at a specific address location? In the BBC micro, the symbol ? is used to denote 'contents of address'. Thus the command PRINT 5 will print the value 5, whilst PRINT ?5 will print the contents of memory location 5. (It corresponds to the command PEEK used by some other systems). Similarly the command ?5 = 6 will save the value 6 in memory 5 — and may crash the system at the same time!

Now get ready with your multimeter again. Set all the user port bits to outputs by typing:

?&FE62 = &FF

(you could use 255 instead of its hexadecimal equivalent &FF). Also type:

?&FE60 = &FF

to set all the bits high. Now check with your meter, and see that PB0, PB1 etc., are all at about + 5 volts. Now type:

?&FE60 = 0

and see that PB0, PB1 etc., have all dropped to 0v. Now, using the values 1, 2, 4, 8, 16, 32, 64 and 128 ensure that you can set the lines high one at a time. Now try various combinations — see why it's easier to use hexadecimal?

Now try configuring the port as an input. Just type:

?&FE62 = 0

and every line will be an input. Enter the program:

```
10  PRINT ?&FE60
20  GOTO 10
```

and run it. As you touch a 0v wire onto each pin PB0, PB1 etc., you will see
the number change from 255. After a short battle of mental arithmetic you
may prefer to change the program to:

```
10  PRINT 255-?&FE60
20  GOTO 10
```

Sinks and sources

You have, of course, noticed that you have had to prod the input with 0v to
change it, not 5v. Each pin has an internal 'pull-up' resistor which if left
alone will hold the input at 5v, and the computer will read it as a '1'. To pull
the input down to a '0' the input signal must be able to 'sink' about 1
milliamp of current. This current corresponds to one 'TTL load', and sets
a limit on the number of logic inputs which a TTL logic gate output can
drive. To have a good 'fan-out', a TTL gate must be able to sink ten or
more milliamps, but does not really need to 'source' any current at all to
work. The pulling-down capability of the logic outputs is therefore much
better than the pulling-up power, although the port-B lines are beefier than
port-A, and can source three milliamps or so compared with port-A's 1
milliamp. (Although the 6522 is a MOS device, it is designed to be TTL
compatible.)

More versatile yet!

Of course that is not the whole story about the 6522. Four of its sixteen
addresses are taken up with data and data direction — that leaves twelve
more on which to build its reputation for versatility. Two pairs of
addresses concern two sixteen-bit counters, which can be used for a variety
of timing functions. Another controls a shift register, used to transfer data
in and out of CB2. A further register, the flag register, indicates the
conditions which could have caused an interrupt, such as timer-expired,
data-handshake etc. Finally two more registers, the Peripheral Control
Register and the Auxiliary Control Register orchestrate the whole variety
show. Even the simple-looking port B has some surprises up its sleeve, for
PB7 can produce a pulse of variable width or a pulse train under the control
of timer 1, whilst PB6 can be used as an input for pulses to be counted by
timer 2.

The shift-register output has a particular use which will appear in Chapter 9; using a certain amount of deviousness it can be persuaded to give a signal which after smoothing will serve to command an analogue servomotor. Of greater immediate interest to Model A owners is how to input an analogue signal from a joystick, and this warrants a short chapter of its own.

Switching mains voltages

Having come to grips with the port, now is the time to put it to some use. A particularly useful device when power-switching is required is the 'solid-state-relay'. This is in fact an opto-isolated triac which will switch an AC mains load of several amps on or off at will. Provided all necessary precautions are taken to avoid stray conductors (or especially fingers) bridging between the signal end and the 'hot' end of the device, the opto-isolation makes it a safe device for connecting to the user port. Connection could hardly be simpler; the + pin is connected to + 5v, whilst the − pin is attached to the PB bit which has been chosen to operate the unit. Whenever this bit is configured as an output, and when the corresponding output data bit is zero, the switch will be on.

The RS number of the 2.5 ampere device is RS 348−431. At a price pushing ten pounds, you may not want to add too many channels. The simple program given below could be made to switch a reading lamp on and off at random times. With simple modifications, the times could be made less random to give the impression of somebody working late, then going to bed. With the addition of a photocell and an ADVAL or two, the system can respond to fading daylight. Beware however that the passing burglar does not deduce that the lamp is flashing the presence of a BBC micro in the house!

```
 10  CLS: PRINT "TIMES IN MINUTES:"
 20  INPUT "MAX ON-TIME " OM
 30  INPUT "MAX OFF-TIME " OFM
 40  INPUT "MIN ON-TIME " OL
 50  INPUT "MIN OFF-TIME " OFL
 60  IF (OL-OM> 0) OR (OFL – OFM> 0) THEN GOTO 10
100  ?&FE62 = 1: REM MAKE BIT 0 AN OUTPUT
200  ?&FE60 = 0: REM TURN ON LIGHT
210  T = OL + (OM-OL)*RND(1): REM BETWEEN OL, OM
220  PROCPATIENCE
300  ?&FE60 = 1: REM TURN OFF LIGHT
310  T = OFL + (OFM-OFL)*RND(1)
320  PROCPATIENCE
```

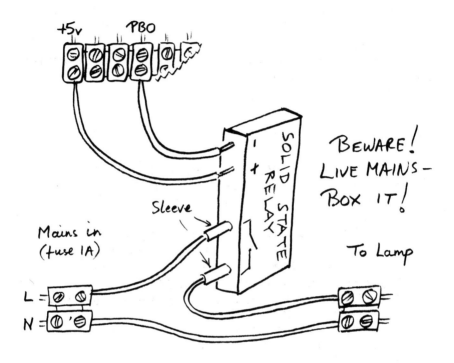

Figure 4.3 Solid state relay for light control

```
 330 GOTO 200
1000 DEF PROCPATIENCE
1010 T = T*60 : REM MAKE SECONDS
1020 FOR I = 1 TO T
1030 A$ = INKEY$(100): REM ONE SECOND DELAY
1040 NEXT
1050 ENDPROC
```

It's a bit primitive as it stands, but I am sure that you will be able to add any extra features you need.

Random Light

```
  10 CLS:PRINT "TIME IN MINUTES :"
  20 INPUT "MAX ON TIME    " OM
  30 INPUT "MAX OFF TIME   " OFM
  40 INPUT "MIN ON TIME    " OL
  50 INPUT "MIN OFF TIME   " OFL
  60 IF (OL-OM>0) OR (OFL-OFM>0) THEN 10
 100 ?&FE62=1:REM MAKE BIT 0 AN OUTPUT
 200 ?&FE60=0:REM TURN ON LIGHT
 210 T=OL+(OM-OL)*RND(1):REM BETWEEN OL,OM
 220 PROCPATIENCE
 300 ?&FE60=1:REM TURN OFF LIGHT
 310 T=OFL+(OFM-OFL)*RND(1)
 320 PROCPATIENCE
 330 GOTO200
1000 DEF PROCPATIENCE
1010 T=T*60 : REM MAKE SECONDS
1020 FOR I=1 TO T
1030   A$=INKEY$(100):REM 1 SECOND DELAY
1040   NEXT
1050 ENDPROC
```

CHAPTER 5
Analogue Input for the Model A

Model A owners will be now be impatient to know how to input a joystick signal without needing to add a fully-fledged analogue-to-digital convertor. The method described here uses no more than a single bit of the user port. The roots of the technique lie in the depths of antiquity — they are at least five years old.

How it works

The old single-chip TV tennis games needed to encode the joystick signals with a minimum of resources. There was no room for analogue-to-digital conversion — the chip would be hard pressed to process the digital value at display speeds anyway. Instead the joystick variable resistance was connected to a capacitor, giving a variable time-constant. Let us consider horizontal bat movement. At the start of each TV line the capacitor was discharged. As the line was then scanned, the capacitor charged up via the joystick resistance. As the capacitor passed the threshold voltage of the input connection, the screen dot brightened to write the image of the bat. In other words, the joystick resistance was converted into a delay, which could be read by a single input bit. Can't we play the same trick with one bit of the user port?

For demonstration purposes try a large value of capacitor first, so that the timing can be done with a loop of BASIC program. Afterwards reduce the capacitor so that machine code will give a swift answer. Start with 1000 microfarads (a 6v electrolytic is actually quite small). Connect this between 0v (− ve end) and PB0. Now enter and run the following program:

```
 10  ?&FE62 = 1: REM Configure PB0 as an output
 20  ?&FE60 = 0: REM Zero output to discharge capacitor
100  C% = 0: REM Set count to zero
110  ?&FE62 = 0: REM PB0 becomes an input, capacitor released
120  IF (?&FE60 AND 1)> 0 THEN 200: REM got to threshold ?
130  C% = C% + 1: REM keep counting
140  GOTO 120: REM round again
200  ?&FE62 = 1: REM discharge the capacitor again
```

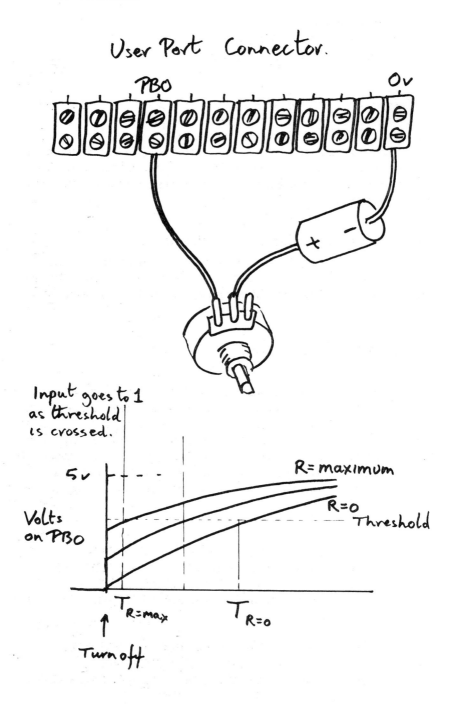

Figure 5.1 Simple analogue input

```
210  PRINT C%
220  A$ = INKEY$ 200: REM brief delay
230  GOTO 100: REM do it all again.
```

The numbers which appear on the screen will depend on the exact value of the capacitor. Disconnect the capacitor and the numbers should fall to zero. Now connect a 2 kilohm potentiometer as a variable resistance in series with the capacitor to PB0 — ie capacitor + ve end to potentiometer 'wiper', one end of potentiometer to PB0, − ve of capacitor to 0v. While the program runs, the number printed should change as the potentiometer shaft is turned.

A high-speed machine-code version

To be generally usable, the routine must be rewritten in machine code (ie assembly language) and should take the form of a function. The following software will enable you to build programs which include such expressions as:

X = FNVAL(1):Y = FNVAL(2)

The values returned will lie between 0 and 255 — not quite up to the standard of the 12-bit A-to-D convertor, but much better than nothing. Early in your program you must include the assembly section — lines 10−200 here. You must also include the function definition as in lines 300−330. The main program here does no more than show the values on the screen, and is of greatest use for selecting the capacitor values. It should take little imagination, however, to modify the program of Chapter 3 to incorporate the new routines.

```
 10 REM USE 2K PORT WITH 2 MICROFARADS
 20 DIM GAP% 100:REM MAKE ROOM FOR THE CODE
 30 FOR I = 0 TO 2 STEP 2 : REM ASSEMBLE 2-PASS
 40 P% = GAP% : REM TELL ASSEMBLER WHERE TO PUT
CODE
 50 [OPT I
 60 .ATOD SEI \INHIBIT MASKABLE INTERRUPTS
 70 TAY \CHANNEL NUMBER IS IN A ON ENTRY
 80 EOR &FE62\SET CORRESPONDING BIT OF DDRB LOW
 90 STA &FE62\TO SET INPUT MODE
100 TYA
```

```
110 LDX #0\CLEAR THE COUNT
120 .LOOP BIT &FE60\LOOP UNTIL INPUT GOES HIGH
130 BNE DONE
140 INX
150 BNE LOOP\OR UNTIL COUNT OVERFLOW
160 LDX #&FF
170 .DONE ORA &FE62\SET PORT BIT TO OUTPUT AGAIN
180 STA &FE62
190 CLI\PERMIT INTERRUPTS AGAIN
200 STX V\PARK THE RESULT IN V
210 RTS\GO HOME
220 .V NOP\LOCATION FOR RESULT
230 ]
240 NEXT I
250 ?&FE60 = 0 : REM SET USER PORT DATA BITS TO ZERO
260 ?&FE62 = 3 : REM SET BITS 0 AND 1 TO OUTPUT MODE
500 PRINT FNVAL(1),FNVAL(2)
510 A$ = INKEY$(10):REM:BRIEF DELAY
520 GOTO 500
1000 DEF FNVAL(X)
1010 A% = X : REM SEND CHANNEL NUMBER TO A
1020 CALL ATOD : REM CALL THE MACHINE CODE
1030 = ?V : REM PICK UP THE RESULT
```

Every so often the processor is 'interrupted' to go off and deal with some housekeeping such as reading the A-to-Ds. In a BASIC program this is not noticeable, but if it happens in the middle of the timing loop above it will mess up the result. The command SEI blocks the interrupt — but always be sure to re-enable it with CLI afterwards, or take the consequences!

Enter the program and set it running. With nothing attached to the user port, two columns of zeros should appear on the screen. Now connect a 2 microfarad capacitor in series with a 2 kilohm potentiometer between PB0 and 0v. You should find that as you turn the potentiometer you can obtain numbers in column 1 which vary from 0 to 255. If the maximum number is less than 255, use a correspondingly larger capacitor. If the smallest number is not 0, use a potentiometer of a higher value of resistance.

Now give PB1 the same treatment, and you have the makings of a joystick. Of course, you can easily increase the number of input channels up to 8, one for each bit of the user port. There is not even any need to modify the program — it will cope with 8 channels as it stands, provided they are called as 1, 2, 4, 8, 16 etc.

The time for caution is when you have other inputs and outputs using the remaining bits of the user port. If you ask for FNVAL(C), and

unfortunately allow C to have the value 240 on entry then the top four bits
of the port will be left configured as outputs. Likewise the value of the
output data may have been disturbed by some other program, and bits 0
and 1 might no longer be zero. In this case you can take out some insurance
by changing line 310 to:

1010 A% = X AND 3

and adding line 1015:

1015 ?&FE60 = ?&FE60 AND 252

Alternatively you may like to make similar modifications to the assembly
instructions, which will result in faster execution than if you enter these
commands in BASIC.

A simple application

Now that Model A owners can read a joystick, they will want to modify the
program of Chapter 3 to use this routine. There are two main problems; the
simplest is the modification of lines 1020 and 1030 of Chapter 3's program
to call FNVAL instead of ADVAL, and a change of the value of SCALE
assigned in line 40 from the old value of 30 to a value of 0.25 — ie the output
from FNVAL is in the range 0 to 255, and must be multiplied by 4 to give
the screen range of 0 to 1000. A little more of a problem is the need to tuck
the assembler section out of the way of the paintwork. Add line 60:

60 GOTO 700

and insert the assembler and housekeeping part of this chapter's program
(lines 10 to 260), renumbered with line numbers from 700 to 950. Then add:

960 GOTO 100

put the definition of FNVAL(X) at lines 1100 to 1130, and you have a
complete program.

A to D — Basic

```
  5 REM 1000UF 1K POT
 10 ?&FE62=1: REM Configure PB0 for output
 20 ?&FE60=0: REM Make output register 0,di
scharge capacitor
100 C%=0
110 ?&FE62=0: REM PB0 becomes input, capaci
tor released
120 IF (?&FE60 AND 1)>0 THEN 200 :REM got to
 threshold?
130 C%=C%+1: REM keep counting
140 GOTO 120: REM round again
200  ?&FE62=1 :REM discharge the capacitor
 again
210 PRINT C%
220 A$=INKEY$ 200: REM brief delay
230 GOTO 100: REM do it again
```

A to D — Assembler

```
 10 REM 2UF 2K POT
 20 DIM GAP% 100
 30 FOR I=0 TO 2 STEP 2
 40   P%=GAP%
 50   [OPT I
 60   .ATOD SEI
 70   TAY
 80   EOR &FE62
 90   STA &FE62
100   TYA
110   LDX #0
120   .LOOP BIT &FE60
130   BNE DONE
140   INX
150   BNE LOOP
160   LDX #&FF
170   .DONE ORA &FE62
180   STA &FE62
190   CLI
200   STX V
210   RTS
220   .V NOP
```

```
 230    ]
 240    NEXT I
 250 ?&FE60=0
 260 ?&FE62=3
 270 GOTO 500
 280
 500 PRINT FNVAL(1),FNVAL(2),FNVAL(4)
 510 A$=INKEY$ 3:GOTO 500
1000 DEF FNVAL(X)
1010 A%=X:CALL ATOD
1020 =?V
```

CHAPTER 6
Stepper Motors and their Use

Stepper motors are a favourite actuator for obtaining motor output. Their drives involve only logic signals, with no need for digital-to-analogue conversion. Until recently only precision 'upper-class' motors were available at an outrageous price, but with the microcomputer and a requirement for low-cost peripherals there has come a demand for cheap stepper motors which the industry has been swift to fulfil. A suitable motor for turtles and micromice is the Philips ID35, distributed by Impex of Richmond at around £12.

Problems and principles

Despite their apparent advantages, stepper motors are not without their problems. They have a firm restriction on their top speed, and the useful torque falls off dramatically as this is approached. Sudden speed changes, even at relatively low speeds, can stall the motor. Unfortunately unless special sensors are added the computer is unaware that the motor has slipped 'out of cog'. All subsequent movements therefore take place with a position error, until a reset manoeuvre is made. Another drawback in a battery-driven system is power consumption; even when stationary a stepper draws as much power as under full load.

Just how does a stepper motor work? The rotor is a permanent magnet, whilst the stator (the fixed case) has a number of electrical windings which when energised create a magnetic field. The field pulls the rotor into line, and by changing the selection of energised windings in a suitable sequence, the rotor is pulled round step by step. When the stepping stops, the rotor is held in position by the magnetic field.

A simple stepper demonstrator

The movement of the permanent-magnetic rotor can be likened to the rotation of a magnetic compass — indeed you can use a compass in an experiment to demonstrate how a stepper motor operates. Obtain a cheap compass — the simple sort with a pointer rather than an ornate card will be best. Wind a coil of 50 turns of fine enamelled copper wire — 36 swg or finer — across the compass. Obviously the wire must not obscure the view of the needle.

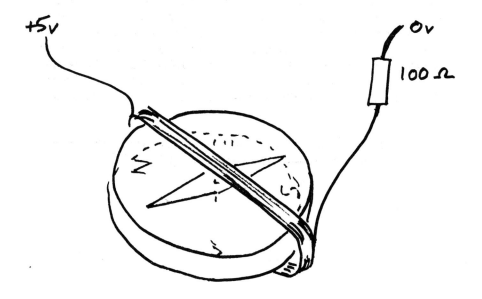

Figure 6.1   Compass and coil

Connect a 47 ohm resistor in series with the coil, and apply 5v across the ends — this can best be found on the user-port connector strip. The needle should line up almost perpendicular to the coil, ie along the axis of the coil. Reverse the applied voltage, and the needle will reverse. Could the coil, and hence the needle, be driven directly from two bits of the user port? Unfortunately the current available from PB0–7 is limited to about three milliamps, and unless you are prepared to wind coils of several hundred turns this will not dominate the effect on the needle of the earth's magnetic field. We must therefore use some amplification — no bad thing in preparing to drive genuine stepper motors. The simplest amplifier consists of just one resistor and one transistor per bit of output — four of each per motor. (Later on we can consider using a Darlington driver chip instead.) A good general purpose PNP transistor is a 2N 3703 (RS 294–334), costing well under one pound per pack of five. First connect just one transistor to your coil, driving it from PB0 via a 1 kilohm resistor as shown in **Figure 6.2**.

Connect the circuit and switch on; nothing should happen to the compass at first. Set the output data register to all-bits-high by typing:

?&FE60 = 255

Then configure bits 0–3 as outputs by typing:

?&FE62 = 15

Still nothing should happen, because the output of PB0 is high, and does not yet sink any current via the transistor base. Now type:

?&FE60 = 255 – 1

This will take PB0 to zero and current will flow into PB0 from + 5v through the transistor base and R1. The transistor will be turned on, applying 5V from the transistor collector to the coil and resistor. The needle should leap into action. Turn the current off again with:

?&FE60 = 255

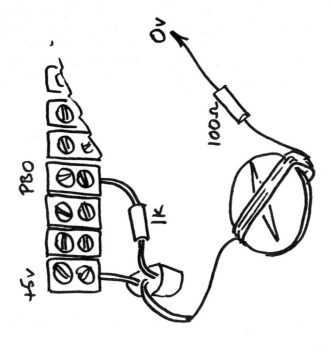

Figure 6.2   Transistor driver

before the resistor R2 starts cooking.

To reverse the needle, we must be able to pass current in the opposite direction. With a circuit as simple as this one, we cannot reverse the current in the wire, and so we need a second coil, wound directly over the top of the first. Wind a further fifty turns of wire, connecting one end to the resistor, and winding in a direction such that the two joined wires become the half-way point of the coil which now has one hundred turns. Connect a twin of the transistor circuit, and drive it from PB1.

Now the commands:

$$?\&FE60 = 255 - 2$$

followed by:

$$?\&FE60 = 255 - 1$$

should drive the compass needle first one way (North, say) and then the other (South). Another command:

$$?\&FE60 = 255$$

will switch off both arms of the coil, and the compass will be left to the mercy of the earth's field.

So far messing about with a compass does not seem to have much to do with motors. But now the plot gets more exciting. Wind another twin coil, also of 50 + 50 turns, over and perpendicular to the first coil. Now when the new coil is connected via two more transistors and driven from PB2 to PB3, the command:

$$?\&FE60 = 255 - 4$$

will cause the needle to point in the new direction. If the first coil caused the needle to point North or South, then the second coil causes the needle to point East or West. By switching on both coils together we can also obtain NE, SE, SW and NW.

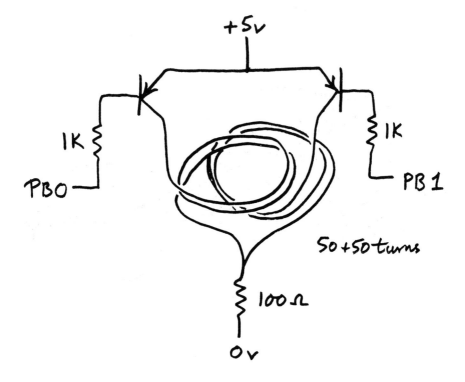

Figure 6.3   Bi-directional drive

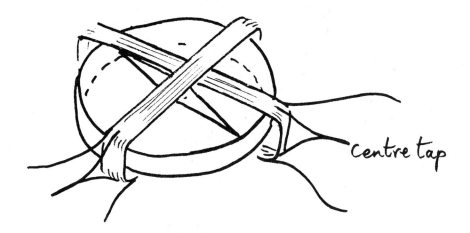

centre tap

Figure 6.4   Two coils

Speed and acceleration control

Enter and run the following program:

```
10 ?&FE62 = 15       : REM PB0 – PB3 ARE OUTPUTS
20 ?&FE60 = 255 – 5  : REM BOTH COILS ON TO GIVE N–E
30 GOSUB 200         : REM 1 SECOND DELAY
40 ?&FE60 = 255 – 9  : REM NOW COILS GIVE N–W
50 GOSUB 200
60 ?&FE60 = 255 – 10 : REM NOW COILS GIVE S–W
70 GOSUB 200
80 ?&FE60 = 255 – 6  : REM N–W
90 GOSUB 200
100 GOTO 20          : REM ROUND AGAIN FOR ANOTHER
REVOLUTION
200 FOR I = 1 TO 2000 : NEXT:RETURN : REM DELAY 1
SECOND OR SO
```

The compass needle should now rotate, if somewhat jerkily, acting as a stepper motor.

Now you can try a variety of numbers in line 200 to set the speed of the motor. You will find that if you aim too high, the motor will not even start. Try accelerating steadily by making the following changes:

```
Add line        5  V = 2000
Change line   200  FOR I = 1 TO V:NEXT
Add line      210  V = V – 1
Add line      220  IF V< 50 THEN V = 50
Add line      230  RETURN
```

Now the delay will reduce progressively until the top speed is reached; try various values in line 220.

The speed will climb very slowly, rushing at the end. A steadier speed-up can be obtained with:

```
210  V = V*.995
```

You are now experimenting with techniques which you will need when you graduate to a genuine stepper motor. Of course the program is still grossly inelegant, and is not exactly versatile. Nevertheless the compass motor will already have taught you some of the pitfalls to look for.

1. Without drive, the motor does not retain its position.
2. Settling to a new position takes the form of a poorly damped oscillation. At certain stepping speeds, there is a resonance so that the oscillations build up; the motor then stalls.
3. Movement at low speeds is 'lumpy'. This can be improved somewhat by doubling up on the applied steps, so that the sequence is N, NE, E, SE, S, SW, W, NW and back to N.
4. Sudden changes of speed will stall the motor.
5. There is no absolute position reference. Everything depends on the motor keeping in step.

Stepper software with some structure

Now let us try to introduce some 'style' into the software so that it will be of more general use. The codes which determine the coil polarities are best held in an array. I have a personal preference for putting all initialisation data at the end of the program, so that it does not obscure listings of the functional part. Thus the program will start with GOTO 10000, and all definitions will start at line 1000.

```
10000  DIM DRIVE(7):FOR I = 0 TO 7
10010  READ J: DRIVE(I) = 255 − J: NEXT I
10020  DATA 1,5,4,6,2,10,8,9
10030  DDR = &FE62:PORT = &FE60:?DDR = 15
10040  HERE = 0
10050  GOTO 100 : REM HOUSEKEEPING DONE
```

If the number of steps to move is held in variable DISTANCE, whilst the direction is held in ROT as a value + / − 1, and if the current position is held in HERE, then an appropriate section of program to command the movement could be:

```
200  PROCMOVE(DISTANCE,ROT,SPEED)
```

where the procedure has been defined as:

59

```
10100 DEFPROCMOVE(D,R,S):IF  (D<1)  OR  (S<1)  THEN
ENDPROC
10110  FOR I = 1 TO D
10120  HERE = HERE + R
10130  ?PORT = DRIVE(HERE AND 7)
10140  FOR J = 1 TO 1000/S:NEXT J
10150  NEXT I
10160  ENDPROC
```

The variable delay of line 10140 might appear a clumsy way to set the speed, but it is effective unless the value of SPEED is excessive. A more elegant technique, that of the 'binary-rate-multiplier', is described in the next chapter. It is useful for coordinating the movements of several steppers, but because of an uneven stepping rate the top speed is reduced.

To complete this program, you can add:

```
10  GOTO 10000
100  PRINT"DISTANCE, ROTATION DIRECTION, SPEED"
110  INPUT DISTANCE, ROTATION, SPEED
210  GOTO 100
```

and you have a demonstration program enabling you to command a move from the keyboard. You should then be able to write a more elaborate program which builds an array of programmed moves and then executes them.

As you will see in the next chapter, a second stepper motor can be added, driven from bits PB4–PB7. This will enable you to make a plotter or a turtle, but will be a bit restrictive for a robot. Chapter 8 includes the addressing techniques which you will need to use if up to eight motors are to be commanded from a single user port.

Power supplies

Before going into any more software detail, let us consider the electronic problems of interfacing one or more genuine stepper motors to the computer. The principles remain the same, but we must now be able to supply much greater currents. These are beyond the permitted drain which can be taken from the micro, and so a separate supply must be provided. You should be able to buy a 1 ampere supply, variable from 4 to 10 volts, for under thirty pounds. Even so, this is scarcely enough current —

although an overload will merely 'fold back' the output. The best answer may be to build the unstabilised supply described in Chapter 1, which will give around three amps output at + 7v and − 7v. Many stepper motors will require 12 volts or more to give of their best, and the power supply can be connected to give a single 14 volt supply — just by using the − 7v terminal as the negative connection and ignoring the centre terminal.

A lazy but risky alternative is to take your life in your hands and use a motor-car battery charger. This will probably give you up to four amps, but will need a larger external capacitor — 10,000 microfarads or so. It will also give poor regulation, and will put nothing better than a four-amp fuse between your circuitry's well-being or annihilation. Still, it's better than buying an endless supply of batteries, unless you can afford rechargeables.

Interfacing hardware

The simple transistor will hardly have enough 'beta' to drive a stepper motor from the earlier circuit. However, you can buy Darlington transistors with much higher gain. They are in fact a pair of transistors in cascade, but have the disadvantage of a higher 'bottoming' voltage — they are less efficient in low voltage circuits. Nowadays it is much more economic to buy multi-function chips than to buy individual transistors, and the RS 307 − 109 chip contains seven Darlingtons, complete with input resistors and protection diodes, for well under two pounds. Murphy's Law gets you, of course, because to drive two stepper motors you need eight outputs, not seven.

Another complication is that these circuits are 'sinks', not sources. The common point of the motor windings must therefore be connected to the positive supply, and the winding will be energised when the user port output bit is high, not low. The line of the computer program setting up the output patterns will have to be changed, leaving out the '255−' inversion, to become

10010 READ J:DRIVE(I) = J:NEXT I:HERE = 0

Moreover the program will have to set ?&FE62 to 15 or 255 as early as possible, so that zeros will be output and the motor will not be incinerated under double its fair share of active currents.

With the change to the program described above, and with the circuit shown in **Figure 6.5**, you should be confident of your ability to drive stepping motors and should be ready to build the simple turtle described in the next chapter.

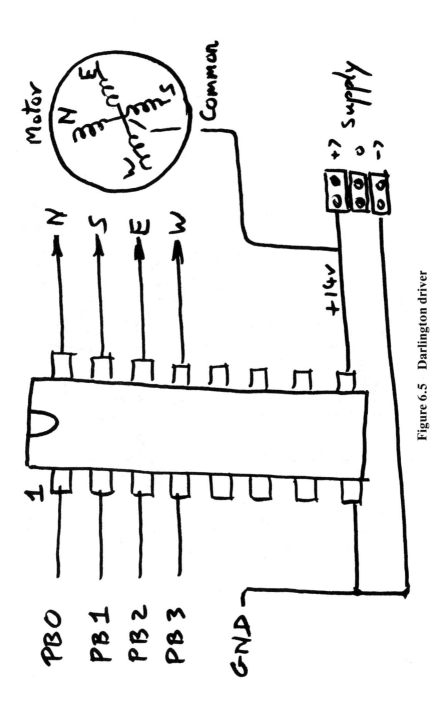

Figure 6.5   Darlington driver

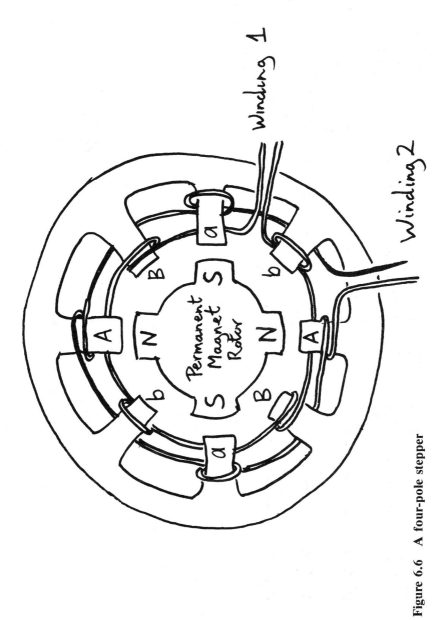

Figure 6.6   A four-pole stepper

Multi-pole steppers

Stepper motors can have as many as 200 steps per revolution. As the inputs are switched through one 'electrical revolution', the motor only rotates through a few degrees. How is this achieved? **Figure 6.6** shows a rotor which, unlike a simple compass needle, has two North and two South poles. The motor coils are no longer wound directly across the rotor, but are wound on pairs of salient poles. When winding 1 is driven in the positive direction, let us say that poles A become South and poles a become North. When instead winding 2 is driven in a positive direction, poles B become South and the rotor is pulled round through 45 degrees. After the windings have been stepped through one electrical revolution, winding 1 will again be driven positively, and the rotor will have made just half a turn. Put more poles on the rotor, and the ratio between electrical steps and rotation angle will increase.

Stepper Motor Drive

```
   10 GOTO 10000
  100 PRINT"DISTANCE, ROTATION DIRECTION, SP
EED"
  110 INPUT DISTANCE,ROTATION,SPEED
  200 PROCMOVE(DISTANCE,ROTATION,SPEED)
  210 GOTO100
10000 DIM DRIVE(7):FORI=0TO7
10010    READJ:DRIVE(I)=J:NEXTI:HERE=0
10020 DATA 1,5,4,6,2,10,8,9
10030 DDR=&FE62:PORT=&FE60:?DDR=15
10040 GOTO 100:REM HOUSEKEEPING DONE
10100 DEF PROCMOVE(D,R,S):IF (D<1) OR (S<1)
 THEN ENDPROC
10110 FOR I=1 TO D
10120    HERE=HERE+R
10130    ?PORT=DRIVE(HERE AND 7)
10140    FOR J=1 TO 1000 STEP S:NEXT J
10150    NEXT I
10160 ENDPROC
```

CHAPTER 7
A Simple Turtle

If you come across an inverted soup bowl, wandering about and perhaps drawing shapes on a large sheet of paper, you have met a Turtle. There is no attempt here to go into the intricacies of turtle graphics; instead the principles of the turtle serve as a good excuse for putting a pair of stepper motors to work.

Turtle fundamentals

The turtle is a simple 'wheelchair' system, propelled by two independent wheels on a diameter. Ball bearings or skids limit the resultant fore-and-aft toppling. To move straight ahead, both wheels rotate in step. To turn on the spot, one wheel rotates forwards while the other rotates backwards at exactly the same rate. If one wheel turns at exactly twice the speed of the other, the turtle will follow a circle with centre one wheel-space from the slower wheel. Accurate movement calls for the motors being driven accurately in step — just the job for stepper motors!

At the centre of a 'genuine' turtle is a retractable pen, so that its perambulations can be used to draw shapes, or even graphs and illustrations. Let us think about that problem later.

Two stepper motors can be driven with little complication from the eight bits of the user port. With the aid of two multi-Darlington chips plus the experience of the last chapter, the task of making the motors rotate should give little trouble. The more difficult part is to make the software 'meaningful', so that a command structure can be based on the desired movements of the turtle without going into the gory details of the number of motor steps required for each gyration. Taking a 'top-down' look at the problem, we want to be able to type "advance, 100" to move 100mm forwards, or perhaps "turn, clockwise, 90". Circles would be nice to add, with perhaps "circle, clockwise, 200, 90" giving 90 degrees of a 200mm radius circle. It might not even be 'over the top' to add Cornu spirals to blend one radius to another but not just at the moment. With graphics in mind, the further commands "pen, up" and "pen, down" complete the set. The task of working out where the turtle would wind up after a given manoeuvre can be performed on the command sequence by another subroutine, if required, although mechanical tolerances mean that the result will not be particularly accurate after a lengthy perambulation.

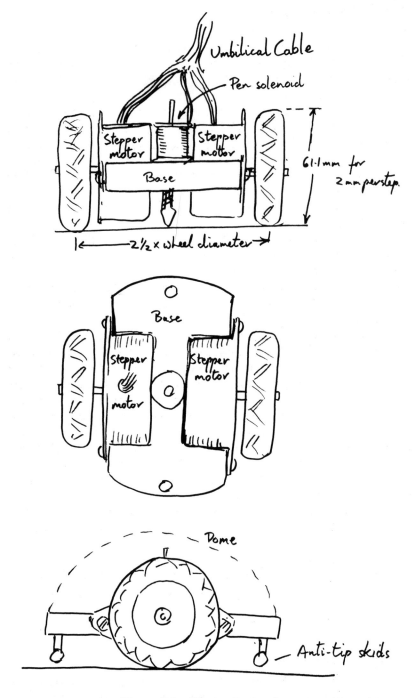

Figure 7.1   Views of a turtle

Mechanical design

The suggested stepper motors are type ID35, made by Philips and distributed by Impex of Richmond at a price of around £12. They have 48 steps per rev., ie 12 electrical revolutions per mechanical revolution. If you drive the motor in half-steps, ie N, NE, E, SE, S, SW, W, NW, you will now have 96 half-steps per revolution of the wheel. Suppose that your wheels are 80mm in diameter, then they will have a circumference of around 250mm and each half-step will give a movement of about 2.6mm. If you don't mind making or trimming your own wheels, then a diameter of $2*96/pi = 61.1$mm will give exactly 2mm per half step — but you would be best to buy the nearest larger size from the model-shop and accept a slightly odd scale factor.

When the motors are driven equally in opposite directions, the turtle rotates about its centre. If each wheel makes one revolution, then the turtle will turn through (diameter-of-wheel/separation-of-wheels) revolutions. Make the separation two-and-a-half times the diameter, and each step will give just one degree. If the motors are driven at unequal speeds, the distance advanced will be given by the average of the (signed) numbers of steps, whilst the turtle will turn through an angle equal to half their difference.

The 'chassis' can be made from plywood or even balsa wood, since it has very little work to do. The skids can be formed from lightweight cupboard ball-catches, although a couple of bent paperclips will really serve the purpose. They should just clear the ground, so that only one touches the ground at a time. Most of the mechanical load will be due to the umbilical cable, and this must be connected to the turtle at a high central point. If you sacrifice some sort of plastic bowl to make a cover, then the cable can safely emerge from a hole in the centre. If however your turtle is naked you should mount a mast in the centre — not too tall, or the turtle will topple. The cable should approach the turtle from above, dangling from a supporting string attached to the ceiling.

At first sight you will need at least a dozen conductors in the cable, five for each motor, two for a pen-lift plus more for any sensors you may add later. At a pinch you can get away with two less, sharing a common positive power line, but this may be a false economy since the resistance of the cable can cause coupling between the motor drives. Ribbon cable is the neatest solution, but far from the cheapest. Perhaps I should recommend a good book on plaiting.

Control strategies

We can make up an 'algorithm' for converting the commands into demanded motor half-steps (from now on, let us call them just 'steps') as follows. Let us assume a wheel diameter of 61 mm and a separation of 2.5*61 = 152.5 mm.

COMMAND	LEFT MOTOR STEPS	RIGHT MOTOR STEPS
Advance	distance/2	distance/2
Turn, cw	+ angle	− angle
Turn, acw	− angle	+ angle
Circle, cw	angle*(radius/115 + 1)	angle*(radius/115 − 1)
Circle, acw	angle*(radius/115 − 1)	angle*(radius/115 + 1)

Now the command interpreter must 'talk to' a motor control module, which will accept commands in the form of the number of steps each motor must move. An extra command, "speed, 20" can adjust a general variable which need not feature in the syntax. Let us use the grammar of a PROCEDURE to command the motors, and let us define this at line 10200 onwards.

Varying the speed of a single motor can be done with a simple variable delay, but to drive two motors at different speeds calls for a different concept, the 'binary-rate-multiplier'. Suppose that the left motor must move 100 steps, whilst the right motor must move only 67. Then we first construct the ratio of the two, in this case 0.67. Each time round the loop we step the left motor, but the right motor may or may not need to step. To make the decision we keep adding the ratio to another variable, T, say. If T is now greater than 1, the motor is stepped and T is reduced by 1. Sounds confusing? Then let's try an example.

LEFT MOTOR POSITION		T	RIGHT MOTOR POSITION		
	0	0		0	
Step	1	.67		0	
Step	2	1.34	Step	1	T *becomes* 0.34
Step	3	1.01	Step	2	T *becomes* 0.01
Step	4	.68	Step	2	
Step	5	1.35	Step	3	T *becomes* 0.35
. . . .					
. . . .					
Step	97	.99	Step	64	
Step	98	1.66	Step	65	T *becomes* 0.66
Step	99	1.33	Step	66	T *becomes* 0.33
Step	100	1.00	Step	67	T *becomes* 0.00

So we arrive at the end of the movement with each motor having taken the correct number of steps. This is the principle behind most graph-plotting routines for drawing oblique straight lines. The result is slightly improved if T starts with the value 0.5, since this causes the 'unevenness' to be shared out symmetrically along the line. In the example above, the only occurrence of three right-motor steps in a row is at the end of the movement; had T started with the value 0.5 they would have occurred in the middle.

Motor control software

We can now define:

```
10200  DEF PROCMOVE(LM,RM): REM LEFT MOTOR,
RIGHT MOTOR
10210  AL = ABS(LM):AR = ABS(RM): REM ABSOLUTE
VALUES
10220  SL = SGN(LM):SR = SGN(RM): REM AND SIGNS OF
DIRECTIONS.
10230  IF AR + AL = 0 THEN ENDPROC: REM NO MOVE, GO
HOME.
10240  IF AR> AL THEN 10400: REM DEAL WITH THIS
SEPARATELY
10250  RATIO = AR/AL: T = 0.5
10260  FOR M = 1 TO AL: REM HERE WE GO
10270  PROCLEFTMOTOR(SL): REM STEP LEFT MOTOR
DIRECTION SL
10280  T = T + RATIO
10290  IF T> 1 THEN PROCRIGHTMOTOR(SR):T = T – 1
10300  NEXT M: ENDPROC: REM THAT'S ALL, GO HOME.

10400  RATIO = AL/AR: T = 0.5: REM RIGHT MOVE> LEFT
MOVE
10410  FOR M = 1 TO AR
10420  PROCRIGHTMOTOR(SR): REM RIGHT EVERY TIME
10430  T = T + RATIO
10440  IF T> 1 THEN PROCLEFTMOTOR(SL):T = T – 1
10450  NEXT M:ENDPROC
```

This still leaves us with the 'bottom-up' task of writing the motor drivers. We start with housekeeping at line 10000:

```
10000 LP = 0:RP = 0:SPEED = 100:REM MOTOR POSITIONS,
SPEED
10010 DIM LMD(7), RMD(7): REM TWO ARRAYS FOR
MOTOR DRIVES
10020 FOR M = 0 TO 7
10030 READ J: LMD(M) = J: RMD(M) = 16*J: NEXT
10040 DATA 1,5,4,6,2,10,8,9
10050 ?&FE62 = 255:?&FE60 = 0:REM CONFIGURE OUTPUTS,
SET TO ZERO
10060 GOTO 100

10500 DEF PROCLEFTMOTOR(SL): REM NOW FOR THE
PROCEDURES
10510 LP = (LP + SL)AND 7: REM NEW POSITION
10520 ?&FE60 = (?&FE60 AND 240) + LMD(LP)
10530 REM MIX NEW LEFT MOTOR DRIVE WITH OLD
RIGHT, OUTPUT
10540 FOR D = I TO 1000 STEP SPEED: NEXT: REM
VARIABLE DELAY
10550 ENDPROC

10600 DEF PROCRIGHTMOTOR(SR)
10610 RP = (RP + SR)AND 7
10620 ?&FE60 = (?&FE60 AND 15) + RMD(RP)
10630 FOR D = 1 TO 1000 STEP SPEED: NEXT
10640 ENDPROC
```

(Using a modicum of cunning, you should be able to rewrite the motor procedures into a single procedure with two arguments SL and SR. You should then be able to tidy up the move procedure to make it less 'lumpy'. The inelegant procedures here are designed to be easier to understand.)

Before adding the 'clever stuff', trouble-shoot these modules with a 'jiffy program':

```
10 GOTO 10000
100 PRINT "LEFT MOTOR, RIGHT MOTOR"
110 INPUT LM,RM
120 PROCMOVE(LM,RM)
130 GOTO 100
```

and if the result does not look too good, try:

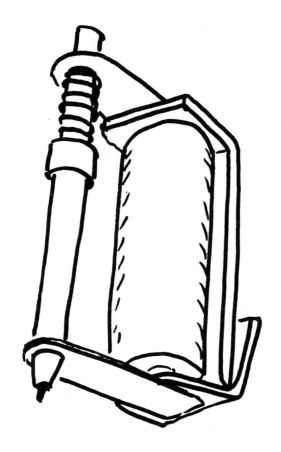

Figure 7.2 Pen lift from post office relay

```
100 SPEED = 10
110 PROCLEFTMOTOR(1): GOTO 110
```

to get down to bedrock. If all else fails, take manual control by setting ?&FE60 to various values, and get out your trusty test meter.

Pen lift

Whilst we are dealing with the 'nuts and bolts', let us have a look at the pen lift. Having thoroughly used up the bits of PB, the only convenient user port bit left is now CB2. Without wishing to tangle too closely with the intricacies of the Peripheral Control Register of the VIA, it is safe to reveal that ?&FE6C = &E0 will set CB2 high, while ?&FE6C = &C0 will set it low. Now CB2 can be wired to another channel of a Darlington chip (using up one of the six spare channels) to give a signal beefy enough to drive a solenoid, and we can add:

```
10700  DEF PROCPEN(P)
10710  IF P = 0 THEN ?&FE6C = &E0:ENDPROC : REM
ENERGISE TO LIFT PEN
10720  ?&FE6C = &C0: REM DEENERGISE, DROP PEN
10730  ENDPROC
```

This does not answer your problem of finding a pen-lift solenoid to drive. A commercial solenoid can easily be bought, but is likely to be heavy and over-powered. It does not take much to lift a ball-point, and even less to lift a felt-tipped pen, and you can substitute a little dexterity for a lot of power consumption. An old post-office relay can, with the removal of the contact assembly, provide more than enough lift. You may need to fiddle a little with the pen height, but provided your wheels are not eccentric you should get acceptable results.

Simple command interpreter

Now we are ready for the command interpreter. This could be written most elegantly and almost incomprehensively with searches in command lists. Instead let us try a 'knife and fork' job, which will simply perform each command immediately. It can be adapted later to memorise and edit a command sequence. The task of inputting the commands is not made easier by the motley assortment of arguments they can take. We have on the one hand "ADVANCE, 200", and on the other "CIRCLE, CW, 45, 150", so the user will welcome some 'user-friendly' guidance. Let us put the parsing routine at 1000:

```
 100  GOTO 1000


1000  PRINT"COMMAND: ";:INPUT A$
1010  IF A$< > "ADVANCE" THEN 1100
1020  PRINT"DISTANCE: " ;:INPUT D
1030  PROCMOVE(D/2,D/2):GOTO1000


1100  IF A$< > "TURN" AND A$< > "CIRCLE" THEN 1300
1110  PRINT"CW/ACW: ";:INPUT B$
1120  PRINT"ANGLE (DEG): ";:INPUT ANG
1130  IF B$ = "ACW" THEN ANG = - ANG
1140  IF A$ = "TURN" THEN PROCMOVE(ANG, - ANG):
GOTO1000


1200  PRINT"RADIUS: ";:INPUT R
1210  IF B$ = "ACW" THEN R = - R
1220  PROCMOVE(ANG*(R/115 + 1),ANG*(R/115 - 1)):
GOTO1000


1300  IF A$< > "SPEED" THEN 1400
1310  PRINT"WAS ";SPEED;", NEW SPEED: ";:INPUT
SPEED:GOTO1000


1400  IF A$< > "PEN" THEN 1500
1410  PRINT"UP/DOWN: ";:INPUT B$
1420  IF B$ = "UP" THEN PROCPEN(0): GOTO1000
1430  PROCPEN(1):GOTO1000

1500  PRINT"SORRY — CAN'T RECOGNISE COMMAND"
1510  PRINT"ADVANCE, TURN, CIRCLE, SPEED, PEN"
1520  GOTO 1000: REM ADD NEW COMMANDS AT 1500
```

As soon as you are happy that this all works, you will want to modify the command structure so that an array of moves is built up, each move executed by a procedure PROCPERFORM(DEED). The routine at 1000 will then plant values of command type, distance/radius and angle into the array, and will have added commands such as PERFORM, STEP, REPEAT, DELETE and ADD to enable you to build up a ballet. You will then also need LOAD and SAVE to preserve the ballet for posterity. If you really get stuck when making these additions, please let me know whether I should include a full program in the next book! You could instead buy a ready-made turtle complete with its software from a specialist firm.

Turtle Program

```
  10 GOTO 10000
 100 GOTO 1000
1000 PRINT "COMMAND :";:INPUT A$
1010 IF A$<>"ADVANCE" THEN 1100
1020 PRINT "DISTANCE :";:INPUT D
1030 PROCMOVE(D/2,D/2):GOTO 1000
1100 IF A$<>"TURN" AND A$<>"CIRCLE" THEN 1
300
1110 PRINT "CW/ACW :";:INPUT B$
1120 PRINT "ANGLE(DEG) :";:INPUT ANG
1130 IF B$="ACW" THEN ANG=-ANG
1140 IF A$="TURN" THEN PROCMOVE(ANG,-ANG):
GOTO 1000
1200 PRINT "RADIUS :";:INPUT R
1210 IF B$="ACW" THEN R=-R
1220 PROCMOVE(ANG*(R/115+1),ANG*(R/115-1))
:GOTO 1000
1300 IF A$<>"SPEED" THEN 1400
1310 PRINT "WAS ";SPEED;", NEW SPEED :";:I
NPUT SPEED:GOTO 1000
1400 IF A$<>"PEN" THEN 1500
1410 PRINT "UP/DOWN :";:INPUT B$
1420 IF B$="UP" THEN PROCPEN(0):GOTO 1000
1430 PROCPEN(1):GOTO 1000
1500 PRINT "SORRY - CAN'T RECOGNISE COMMAN
D."
1510 PRINT "ADVANCE, TURN, CIRCLE, SPEED,
PEN"
1520 GOTO 1000 :REM ADD NEW COMMANDS AT 15
00
10000 LP=0:RP=0:SPEED=100:REM MOTOR POSITIO
NS, SPEED
10010 DIM LMD(7),RMD(7): REM TWO ARRAYS FOR
 MOTOR DRIVES
10020 FOR M=0 TO 7
10030    READ J:LMD(M)=J:RMD(M)=16*J:NEXT
10040 DATA 1,5,4,6,2,10,8,9
```

```
10050 ?&FE62=255:?&FE60=0:REM CONFIGURE OUT
PUTS, SET TO ZERO
10060 GOTO 100
10200 DEF PROCMOVE(LM,RM):      REM LEFT MOTO
R, RIGHT MOTOR
10210 AL=ABS(LM):AR=ABS(RM):    REM ABSOLUTE
 VALUES
10220 SL=SGN(LM):SR=SGN(RM):    REM AND SIGNS
 OF DIRECTIONS
10230 IF AR+AL=0 THEN ENDPROC:REM NO MOVE,
 GO HOME
10240 IF AR>AL THEN 10400:      REM DEAL WITH
 THIS SEPERATELY
10250 RATIO=AR/AL:T=0.5
10260 FOR M=1 TO AL:            REM HERE WE GO
10270    PROCLEFTMOTOR(SL):  REM STEP LEFT M
OTOR DIRECTION SL
10280    T=T+RATIO
10290    IF T>1 THEN PROCRIGHTMOTOR(SR):T=T-1
10300    NEXT M
10310 ENDPROC: REM THAT'S ALL, GO HOME
10400 RATIO=AL/AR:T=0.5: REM RIGHT MOVE > LE
FT MOVE
10410 FOR M=1 TO AR
10420    PROCRIGHTMOTOR(SR):   REM RIGHT EVERY
 TIME
10430    T=T+RATIO
10440    IF T>1 THEN PROCLEFTMOTOR(SL):T=T-1
10450    NEXT M
10460 ENDPROC
10500 DEF PROCLEFTMOTOR(SL):    REM NOW FOR
 THE PROCEDURES
10510 LP=(LP+SL) AND 7:          REM NEW POSI
TION
10520 ?&FE60=(?&FE60 AND 240)+LMD(LP)
10530 REM MIX NEW LEFT MOTOR DRIVE WITH OLD
 RIGHT, OUTPUT
10540 FOR D=1 TO 1000 STEP SPEED:NEXT:REM V
ARIABLE DELAY
10550 ENDPROC
10600 DEF PROCRIGHTMOTOR(SR)
10610 RP=(RP+SR) AND 7
10620 ?&FE60=(?&FE60 AND 15)+RMD(RP)
10630 FOR D=1 TO 1000 STEP SPEED:NEXT
```

```
10640 ENDPROC
10700 DEF PROCPEN(P)
10710 IF P=0 THEN ?&FE6C=&E0:ENDPROC:REM ENE
RGISE TO LIFT PEN
10720 ?&FE6C=&C0:                         REM DEE
NERGISE, DROP PEN
10730 ENDPROC
```

CHAPTER 8
Interfacing a Robot

A 'fully-fledged' robot has seven degrees of freedom, that is to say it requires seven independent motors to drive it. The 'end effector' (a fancy term for 'hand') must be able to move in three dimensions, and for any given position it should be able to swivel about three more axes. A further channel is needed for 'open' or 'close', although this is often a simple on/off valve working a pneumatic gripper. Educational robots such as the Armdroid sacrifice one of the 'wrist' axes, but give continuous grip movement. This reduces the number of channels to six. If these are driven by stepper motors, how can we interface them to the computer? In the last chapter, two channels of stepper motor were interfaced to the user port with the use of all eight bits, so for six channels we must find some new technique to command them all. It is necessary to include an address as part of the user-port data, which can be decoded within the robot itself.

Multi-stepper control

The user port provides eight bits; a stepper motor needs four bits to define a half-step position (unless you are happy interfacing using the scale of three: N, off, S). That leaves four bits for housekeeping. From three of these bits, an address can be constructed to address eight channels. The addressed channel will now capture the motor signals in a four-bit latch, and carry on driving the motor lines until told to do otherwise. Now we need a 'strobe' signal as well, so that we can tell the circuitry 'the motor lines have finished changing, the address lines are settled, catch this data now and use it.'

A logical way to allocate the user-port connections is as follows:

PB0	PB1	PB2	PB3	PB4	PB5	PB6	PB7
---------- Channel ---------			N--------S---------E----------W				Strobe

Since the strobe will be active when low, the procedure for outputting a new command is as follows:

1. Look up the code for the desired motor position.
2. Add on the channel number, hold the result in X, say.
3. Set the strobe bit (bit 7) high in X.
4. Output X to the user port.
5. Set bit 7 of X low; output X to the user port.
6. Set bit 7 of X high again, output X to the user port.

Putting the algorithm into software

Let us adopt our usual technique of defining procedures 'up in the sky', with housekeeping at 10000:

```
10000 DIM  DRIVE(7):  REM  VALUES  WITH  STROBE
ALREADY HIGH
10010 FOR I = 0 TO 7: READ J: DRIVE(I) = 8*J + 128: NEXT
10020 DATA 1,5,4,6,2,10,8,9
10030 MASK = 127:  ?&FE60 = 128:  ?&FE62 = 255:REM  MAKE
OUTPUTS
11040 DEF PROCROBOT(CHANNEL,VLUE)
11050 X = DRIVE(VLUE AND 7) + CHANNEL
11060 ?&FE60 = X
11070 ?&FE60 = X AND MASK
11080 ?&FE60 = X
11090 ENDPROC
```

This routine takes one or two short cuts from the algorithm above, and will simply set up one motor drive to command a given position.

Simultaneous movements

We now want a routine which will set up all six channels of the robot, and will interpolate a manoeuvre so that all channels can be made to move at once. This is another task for the 'binary-rate-multiplier', this time firing on six cylinders. Let us suppose that our starting position is HERE. This must be an array with six elements, one for each motor axis. Suppose also that the destination is held in TARGET. Then we can work through all six axes, finding which one demands the greatest change. Now it is a straightforward job to calculate the ratios, and to make a step according to the overflow of a register, just as in the last chapter.

```
10100 DIM HERE(5),TARGET(5),RATE(5),WAY(5),REG(5)
10110 FOR I = 0 TO 5:HERE(I) = 0:REG(I) = .5:
PROCROBOT(I,0):NEXT
```

```
10120  SPEED = 100
10900  GOTO 100 : REM END OF HOUSEKEEPING

11120  DEF PROCMOVE: REM MOVE FROM HERE TO
TARGET
11130  RMAX = 0:FOR I = 0 TO 5
11140  RATE(I) = ABS(TARGET(I) – HERE(I)):REM
DISTANCE AND
11150  WAY(I) = SGN(TARGET(I) – HERE(I)):REM
DIRECTION EACH AXIS
11160  IF RATE (I)> RMAX THEN RMAX = RATE(I): REM
FIND MAX DISTANCE
11170  NEXT:IF RMAX = 0 THEN ENDPROC: REM NO MOVE
11180  FOR I = 0 TO 5
11190  RATE(I) = RATE(I)/RMAX:NEXT: REM RATES NOW
IN RANGE 0 TO 1

11200  FOR R = 1 TO RMAX: REM NOW WE ARE READY TO
MOVE
11210  FOR CHAN = 0 TO 5
11220  REG(CHAN) = REG(CHAN) + RATE(CHAN)
11230  IF REG(CHAN)< 1THEN 11260
11240  REG(CHAN) = REG(CHAN) – 1:HERE(CHAN) = HERE
(CHAN) + WAY(CHAN)
11250  PROCROBOT(CHAN,HERE(CHAN))
11260  NEXT CHAN
11270  FOR I = 0 TO 1000 STEP SPEED:NEXT:REM DELAY
11280  NEXT R
11290  ENDPROC: REM NOW HERE = TARGET
```

The command level routine

Now the following simple program will execute a string of manoeuvres:

```
  10  GOTO 10000:REM INITIALISE
 100  GOTO 5000
5000  IF NP = 0 THEN GOTO 100:REM NO POINTS
5010  FOR P = 1 TO NP
5020  FOR I = 0 TO 5;TARGET(I) = PNT(P,I):NEXT
5030  PROCMOVE
5040  NEXT P
5050  GOTO 100
```

Spotted any problems? Where have the values of PNT(P,I) come from? The values can be read from tape or disk, or entered as data statements, but that would rather go against the spirit of robotics. To start off with, the values should be recorded from actual movements of the robot. An array of keys can be assigned as a 'super joystick' for Up, Down, Forwards, Backwards, Left, Right, Wrist bend and vice versa, Wrist turn + Y, Open hand, Close hand. Add to these Point to record a coordinate, and End teach to exit from 'teach' mode, and you have the start of a system. A second 'menu' can give options Teach, Perform, Repeat, Save (tape or disk), Input (from tape or disk). If you really feel ambitious you can add Edit, to add, modify or delete points. How do we implement these wonderful functions? Let us make a start with 'teach'.

Teach-mode robot programming

It is important to display a menu of keys on the screen — nothing is more frustrating than having to guess what imput is expected.

```
100 CLS:PRINT TAB(0,5);"Teach,    Perform,"
110 PRINT "Repeat,   Clear,"
120 PRINT "Save,    Input"
130 A$ = GET$: REM WAIT FOR A KEY-PRESS
140 I = INSTR("TPRCSI",A$):IF I = 0 THEN 100; REM DUFF
KEY
150 ON I GOTO 1000,5000,5100,2000,6000,7000
160 REM MAKE UNWRITTEN ROUTINES "GOTO 100"

1000 CLS:PRINT TAB(0,5);"Up    Down"
1010 PRINT"Left    Right"
1020 PRINT"Forward    Back"
1030 PRINT"Wrist — V"
1040 PRINT"Turn — Y"
1050 PRINT"Open    Close"
1060 PRINT"Point    End teach"
1070 PRINT:FOR I = 0 TO 5
1080 PRINT HERE(I):NEXT
1090 *FX15,0
1100 A$ = GET$:REM REPEATS HAVE BEEN CLEARED
1110 IF A$ = "E" THEN GOTO 100
1120 IF A$< > "P" THEN 1150
1130 NP = NP + 1:IF NP> MP THEN 1000: REM TOO MANY
POINTS
1140 FOR I = 0 TO 5: PNT(I,NP) = HERE(I):NEXT
1150 J = INSTR("UDLRFBWVTYOC",A$):IF J = 0 THEN 1000
```

```
1160  FOR I = 0 TO 5
1170  TARGET(I) = HERE(I) + COMMAND(J,I):NEXT
1180  PROCMOVE:GOTO 1000
```

Where did that COMMAND come from, then?! It had to be set up during initialisation, and relates the channel number to the chosen command in the form of a vector of increments. If the main rotation axis is channel 0, then the vector for Left will be 1,0,0,0,0,0 — whilst Right will be −1,0,0,0,0,0. Move than one axis can change at a time — necessary since the 'Armdroid' is wired so that wrist swivel and tilt are a combination of two motors. Almost every Armdroid I have met has a different allocation of channels, and whether +1 is up or down is anybody's guess. The data statements which follow will therefore need nobbling in the light of experiment.

```
10300  NP = 0:MP = 20:REM  MAX  NUMBER  OF  POINTS —
CHANGE AD LIB
10310  DIM PNT(MP,5): REM MAKE ROOM FOR POINTS
10320  DIM COMMAND(12,5)
10330  FOR  J = 1 TO 12:REM FOR EACH COMMAND KEY
UDLRFBWVTYOC
10340  FOR I = 0 TO 5:READ COMMAND(J,I):NEXT:NEXT
10350  DATA 0,  1,  0,  0,  0,  0:REM U
10360  DATA 0, −1,  0,  0,  0,  0:REM D
. . . . . . . . . . . . . . . . . . . .
. . . . . . . . . . . . . . . . . . . .
10410  DATA 0,  0,  0, −1,  1,  0:REM W
10420  DATA 0,  0,  0,  1,  1,  0:REM V
. . . . . . . . . . . . . . . . . . . .
10470  REM  DATA  ABOVE  IS  BOGUS — SORT  OUT
CHANNELS YOURSELF!
10500  GOTO 100
```

By now you should be getting an idea of how to put the rest of the program together. Repeat will look rather like Perform, except that it will keep on looping until a key is pressed:

```
5100  IF NP = 0 THEN GOTO 100
5110  FOR P = 1 TO NP
5120  FOR I = 0 TO 5
```

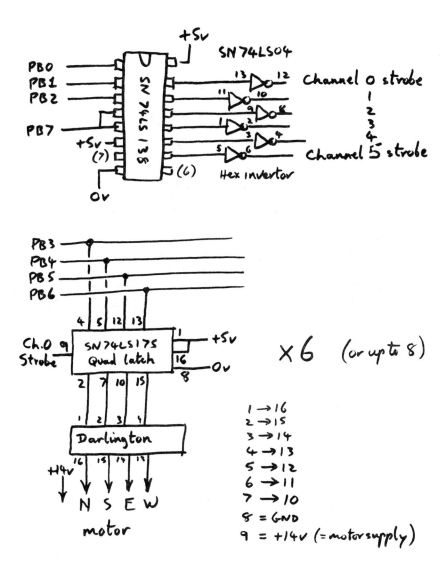

Figure 8.1   Decoder, latches and Darlington driver (6 axis robot)

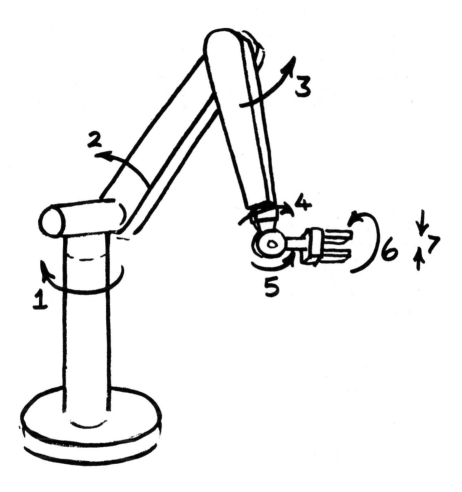

Figure 8.2   Axes of a 'conventional' robot

```
5130  TARGET(I) = PNT(P,I):NEXT
5140  PROCMOVE
5150  NEXT P
5160  IF INKEY$(0)> "" THEN GOTO 100
5170  GOTO 5110
```

and

```
2000  NP = 0:GOTO 100:REM CLEAR
```

You should be able to manage the rest by yourself. Even if you use only the program listed here, you will be able to teach the robot a routine which it will perform with interpolated movements. I do not pretend that the execution will be fast — you will soon want to perform the 'binary-rate-multiplier' functions in machine-code, and include a ramp speed-up routine to achieve top speed without breaking away. Some elegant programs (eg MEMROB, written in collaboration with Tim Dadd and distributed by Colne for using an Armdroid with a PET) link the interpolation and output functions to the computer's interrupt, and communicate between BASIC and machine code by planting values in an array of variables. In this way, the BASIC part can do its 'thinking', working out the speed ratios for the next move at the same time as the present move is being made. The listing of MEMROB has baffled multitudes, and has little teaching value.

Building your own robot

So far this chapter has dug very deeply into the software aspects of robot control, and has neglected the hardware problems. If you intend to use an 'off-the-shelf' robot like the Armdroid, the only problem is the connecting cable. I have specified the BBC's end of the cable, and the robot's handbook will tell you the rest. If on the other hand you want to do-it-yourself, you will first need half a dozen stepper motors. The ID35 mentioned in the last chapter will do nicely — it is the one used in the Armdroid. The Darlington drivers have also been covered pretty thoroughly there. That leaves only the channel decoders and the 4-bit latches — and the power supply. The supply detailed in Chapter 1 should be adequate, and will cost less than a single stepper motor. A suggested circuit diagram is drawn in **Figure 8.1**.

For a do-it-yourself mechanical design, you can either follow close on the heels of the commercial robots, or you can be more adventurous. When you start to examine the number of ways you can link six motors together, the choice is amazing. Your geometry can be cartesian, polar, cylindrical-polar, or a variety of strange hybrids. Let us start by looking at the 'conventional' robots.

Robot anatomy

The first axis of movement is a rotation of the whole assembly about the vertical. You can 'humanise' this by thinking of it as swivelling about the waist. Next, the 'shoulder' joint allows the arm to tilt up and down, so that using these two motors alone the hand could reach any point on the surface of a sphere. Next comes the elbow joint. As this bends, the arm is effectively shortened, although the hand now moves in a way which needs more and more trigonometry to describe it. In principle, the robot should now be able to reach any point within a sphere, but if, for example, the upper arm is not the same length as the forearm there will be some unreachable zones. The wrist joint should now be able to swivel both up-and-down and left-to-right. The Unimation Puma instead uses a movement like the human wrist, where the up-and-down hinge is an axis which can in turn swivel about the line of the forearm. The Armdroid leaves one of these movements out. Now the Puma can in effect line up a screwdriver with a screw in any position; the final axis twists the screwdriver to drive the screw.

Some sophisticated robots such as the Puma perform laborious computations, allowing the user to specify that the hand should move in a straight line and that the tool should not rotate in space. New positions are calculated for the motor axes up to forty times per second, and the movement is then smoothed out by 'rate control' similar to the techniques described earlier. It is a challenging exercise to try!

Even when the geometry is settled, there are many ways to connect the motors to the axes. The Puma uses brute force, so that the entire leverage of the arm and its load will appear at the shoulder joint. The Armdroid on the other hand uses a cunning bit of string-work, so that, as the shoulder rotates the upper arm, the forearm remains parallel to its former position. This effectively halves the leverage of the load on the shoulder motor — although it does not do a lot for the string which is annoyingly apt to break.

The IBM robot is cartesian, and bears a strong resemblance to an overgrown graph plotter for controlling the X and Y axes. The Z axis is an even more overgrown pen-lift, raising and lowering a bar which can rotate to provide the first of the wrist axes. All the problems of straight-line movement are solved at a stroke, but tracks and pulleys are now needed in place of pivots and levers.

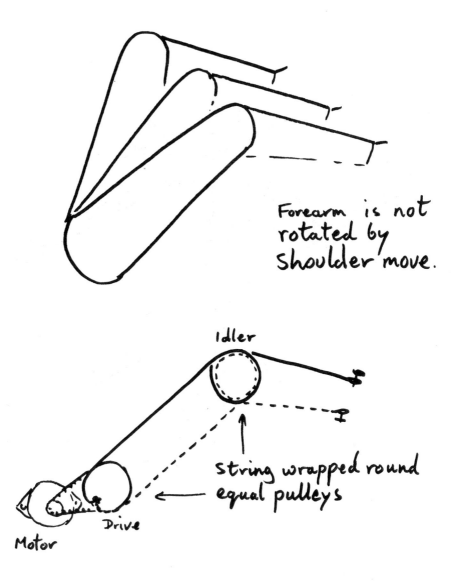

Forearm is not rotated by shoulder move.

Idler

string wrapped round equal pulleys

Drive

Motor

Figure 8.3   Stringing to obtain parallel forearm movement

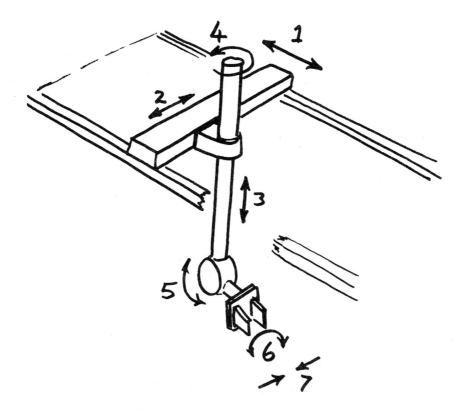

Figure 8.4   Cartesian robot arrangement

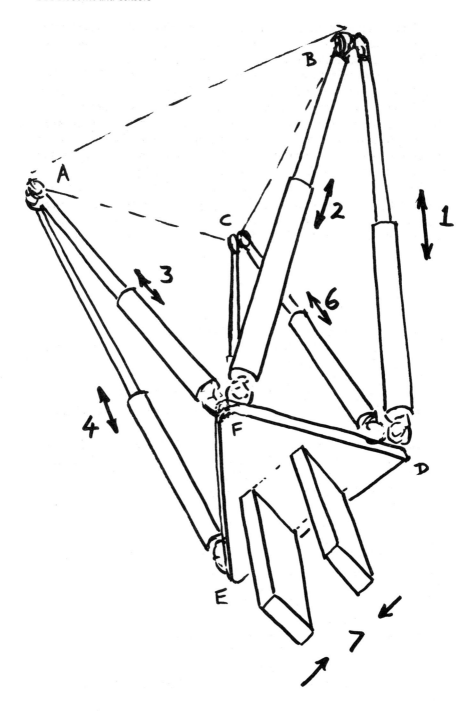

Figure 8.5 A variation of the 'Gadfly'

When computing power is let loose, anything goes. Considerable industrial research is being put into a device using six extending rods, driven by motors and leadscrews. Imagine a triangle ABC fixed to the floor, with the tool attached to a movable triangular plate DEF. The plate is held up by six rods, AE, AF, BF, BD, CD and CE. As these vary in length, so the plate can be moved in three dimensions and rotated about three axes. If you have an idle moment, calculate the relationship between the lengths and the position of the plate, or more especially the lengths required to place the plate in any particular position — a prize is offered for the simplest solution! No wonder it is called the 'Gadfly'.

These variations hardly scratch the surface of the possible combinations. If you connect up the six stepper motor channels, you can try any number of 'lash-ups' using cardboard, string and balsa wood before immortalising your design in aluminium or steel. Good luck!

Robot Program

```
  10 GOTO 10000:REM INITIALISE
 100 CLS:PRINT TAB(0,5);"Teach,      Perform,"
 110 PRINT "Repeat,    Clear,"
 120 PRINT "Save,         Input,"
 130 A$=GET$:REM WAIT FOR A KEY-PRESS
 140 I=INSTR("TPRCSI",A$):IF I=0 THEN 100:
 REM DUFF KEY
 150 ON I GOTO 1000,5000,5100,2000,6000,7000
 160 REM MAKE UNWRITTEN ROUTINES "GOTO 100"
1000 CLS:PRINT TAB(0,5);"Up          Down"
1010 PRINT "Left         Right"
1020 PRINT "Forward     Back"
1030 PRINT "Wrist    - V"
1040 PRINT "Turn     - Y"
1050 PRINT "Open        Close"
1060 PRINT "Point      End teach"
1070 PRINT:FOR I=0 TO 5:
1080    PRINT HERE(I):NEXT
1090 *FX 15,0
1100 A$=GET$:REM REPEATS CLEARED
1110 IF A$="E" THEN 100
1120 IF A$<>"P" THEN 1150
1130 NP=NP+1:IF NP>MP THEN 1000 :REM TOO MA
NY POINTS
1140 FOR I=0 TO 5:PNT(I,NP)=HERE(I):NEXT
```

```
1150 J=INSTR("UDLRFBWVTYOC",A$):IF J=0 THEN
  1000
1160 FOR I=0 TO 5
1170    TARGET(I)=HERE(I)+COMMAND(J,I):NEXT
1180 PROCMOVE:GOTO 1000
2000 NP=0:GOTO 100:REM CLEAR
5000   IF NP=0 THEN 100:REM NO POINTS
5010 FOR P=1 TO NP
5020    FOR I=0 TO 5:TARGET(I)=PNT(P,I):NEXT
5030    PROCMOVE
5040    NEXT P
5050 GOTO 100
5100 IF NP=0 THEN 100
5110 FOR P=1 TO NP
5120    FOR I=0 TO 5
5130       TARGET(I)=PNT(P,I):NEXT
5140    PROCMOVE
5150    NEXT P
5160 IF INKEY$0>"" THEN 100
5170 GOTO 5110
6000 REM WRITE SAVE ROUTINE HERE
6010 GOTO 100
7000 REM WRITE INPUT ROUTINE HERE
7010 GOTO 100
10000 DIM DRIVE(7): REM VALUES WITH STROBE
 ALREADY HIGH
10010 FOR I=0 TO 7:READ J:DRIVE(I)=8*J+128:
 NEXT
10020 DATA 1,5,4,6,2,10,8,9
10030 MASK=127:?&FE60=128:?&FE62=255:REM MA
KE OUTPUTS
10100 DIM HERE(5),TARGET(5),RATE(5),WAY(5),
REG(5)
10110 FOR I=0 TO 5:HERE(I)=0:REG(I)=.5:PROC
ROBOT(I,0):NEXT
10120 SPEED=100
10300 NP=0:MP=20:REM MAX NUMBER OF POINTS -
 CHANGE AD LIB
10310 DIM PNT(MP,5):REM MAKE ROOM FOR POINTS
10320 DIM COMMAND(12,5)
10330 FOR J=1 TO 12:REM FOR EACH COMMAND KEY
 UDLRFBWVTYOC
10340    FOR I=0 TO 5:READ COMMAND(J,I):NEXT:
NEXT
```

```
10350 DATA  0, 1, 0, 0, 0, 0 :REM U
10360 DATA  0,-1, 0, 0, 0, 0 :REM D
10370 DATA  1, 0, 0, 0, 0, 0 :REM L
10380 DATA -1, 0, 0, 0, 0, 0 :REM R
10390 DATA  0, 0, 1, 0, 0, 0 :REM F
10400 DATA  0, 0,-1, 0, 0, 0 :REM B
10410 DATA  0, 0, 0,-1, 1, 0 :REM W
10420 DATA  0, 0, 0, 1,-1, 0 :REM V
10430 DATA  0, 0, 0, 1, 1, 0 :REM T
10440 DATA  0, 0, 0,-1,-1, 0 :REM Y
10450 DATA  0, 0, 0, 0, 0, 1 :REM O
10460 DATA  0, 0, 0, 0, 0,-1 :REM C
10470 REM DATA ABOVE IS BOGUS !!!
10480 REM SORT OUT CHANNELS YOURSELF
10900   GOTO 100:REM END OF HOUSE KEEPING
11040 DEF PROCROBOT(CHANNEL,VLUE)
11050 X=DRIVE(VLUE AND 7)+CHANNEL
11060 ?&FE60=X
11070 ?&FE60=X AND MASK
11080 ?&FE60=X
11090 ENDPROC
11120 DEF PROCMOVE: REM MOVE FROM HERE TO TA
RGET
11130 RMAX=0:FORI=0TO5
11140   RATE(I)=ABS(TARGET(I)-HERE(I)):REM
 DISTANCE AND
11150   WAY(I)=SGN(TARGET(I)-HERE(I)):REM D
IRECTION EACH AXIS
11160   IF RATE(I)>RMAX THEN RMAX=RATE(I):RE
M FIND MAX DISTANCE
11170   NEXT:IF RMAX=0 THEN ENDPROC:   REM NO
 MOVE
11180 FORI=0TO5
11190   RATE(I)=RATE(I)/RMAX:NEXT:REM RATE
 NOW IN RANGE 0 TO 1
11200 FOR R=1 TO RMAX:REM NOW WE ARE READY
 TO MOVE
11210   FOR CHAN=0TO5
11220     REG(CHAN)=REG(CHAN)+RATE(CHAN)
11230     IF REG(CHAN)<1 THEN 11260
11240     REG(CHAN)=REG(CHAN)-1:HERE(CHAN)=
HERE(CHAN)+WAY(CHAN)
11250     PROCROBOT(CHAN,HERE(CHAN))
11260     NEXT CHAN
```

```
11270    FOR I=0 TO 1000 STEP SPEED:NEXT:REM
  DELAY
11280    NEXTR
11290 ENDPROC :REM NOW HERE=TARGET
```

CHAPTER 9
Analogue Output and Position Servos

Despite the advantage of ease of interfacing, the stepper motor has no absolute position reference and runs into more problems when speedy response is necessary. The analogue servo can take its reference from a simple potentiometer, although much more sophisticated devices such as synchros and encoders can be used. The 'feed-back' signal is subtracted from the command signal, and the difference represents the position error of the servo. The servomotor is now driven in proportion to the error, so that it moves to reduce it. When the required position is reached, the motor ceases to require power. On the debit side, if there is a standing force load on the motor it will have a persistent error, the value of error needed to give a drive equal to the force. To minimise this error, the servo 'loop' must be 'stiff', that is to say a small error must give a large motor torque. This raises even more problems, since a small error can cause enough torque for the motor to pick up speed, and sprint past the target to come to rest with a larger error on the other side. Then of course it spins back again, and again ... The servo has started to oscillate.

Feedback and stability

To avoid oscillation, either the stiffness must be reduced or a velocity signal must be added. A velocity term winds down the motor drive as it picks up speed, so that for any given error there is a speed at which the servo is content to freewheel. If the freewheeling speed is exceeded, the servo drive acts in reverse to slow down the motion. Thus if the right mixture of position and velocity is made, the servo comes briskly to rest at the desired position. A velocity or 'tacho' signal can be expensive, but there are ways of obtaining a similar effect more cheaply. A certain amount of velocity feed-back comes from the motor itself, in the form of the 'back-emf' generated by the rotation of the DC motor. This limits the speed up to which the motor will run in response to a given amplifier output voltage, and adds the necessary dose of damping to a low-stiffness system. As the 'gain' of the control loop (ie the voltage out per unit of position error) is increased, so this self-damping becomes less effective. Ultimately the system is 'bang-bang', driving flat out for the slightest error, and without

93

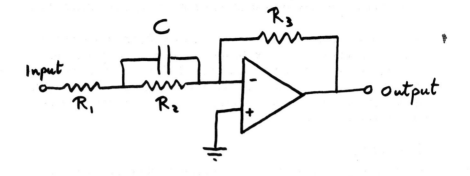

$$\text{High frequency gain} = \frac{R_3}{R_1}$$

$$\text{Low frequency gain} = \frac{R_3}{R_1 + R_2}$$

Step response (negative step input):

Figure 9.1   Phase advance

the addition of a velocity signal to the input of the amplifier, oscillation is inevitable.

A high-power sophisticated servo will have a separate 'tacho' to give a speed signal. However this need be no more exotic than another much smaller motor connected to the main motor shaft and acting as a voltage generator. This sort of system is simple to design, and can be made extremely stiff, but for educational robots the cost of doubling-up on the motors is worth avoiding.

Phase advance

So what other possibilities are there? A substantial increase in stiffness, retaining stability, can be obtained using 'phase-advance'. The feedback resistor is split into two series resistors, and a capacitor is connected across one of these. Since the current in a capacitor is proportional to rate-of-change of voltage, the feedback signal current into a 'virtual-earth' amplifier will include a term due to rate-of-change of error position — a velocity term. Unfortunately phase-advance also magnifies the effect of any noise on the signals, and if the motors are driven from the same power supply that energises the position potentiometer you will soon find oscillation aided and abetted by the power supply lines themselves.

Tacho signal from back-e.m.f.

A more cunning technique is to use the motor back-emf again, but to separate it from the voltage caused by the drive-current. This involves the use of a resistance bridge and a differential amplifier — in fact consisting of no more than three resistors to complete the bridge, and one more resistor plus a fifty-pence TL081 chip. This can be very effective if enough care is taken to balance the bridge, but setting up can be fiddly.

A simple circuit

For now, be content to put together a slightly less crisp servo system which will probably do all you need. A servo module containing motor, gearbox and feedback potentiometer can be bought from a model shop for ten to twenty pounds. The motor used to try out this design was a Skyleader SRC 4BB. A drive amplifier can be made from a single-chip 759 power operational-amplifier (RS number 303–258), and the power supply described in Chapter 1 can be connected to give $+7v$ (or so) and $-7v$ outputs. Your only problem is how to obtain an analogue drive signal from the BBC computer. Before facing that one, get the servo loop working with a command signal taken from a second potentiometer. Connect the new potentiometer (value 1 kilohm) between the 0v and $+5v$ positions of the user port connector-strip, taking the command signal from the centre

Motor drive

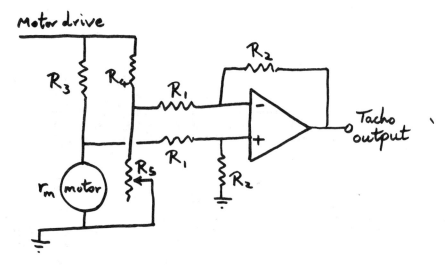

R_S is adjusted to make $\dfrac{R_S}{R_4} = \dfrac{r_m}{R_3}$,

where r_m is motor resistance.

R_3 is chosen to be less than r_m to avoid loss of motor power.

Output $\simeq \dfrac{R_2}{R_1} \times \dfrac{R_3}{R_3 + r_m} \times$ back e.m.f.

(For 10Ω motor, try $R_3 = 3.3\,\Omega$, $R_4 = 2.2\,k\Omega$
$R_1 = 10k\Omega$, $R_2 = 39k\Omega$, $R_S = 1k\Omega$ potentiometer)

Figure 9.2   Tacho signal from motor back e.m.f.

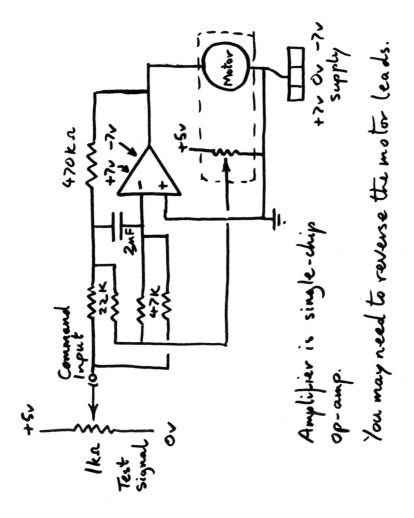

Figure 9.3   Servo amplifier

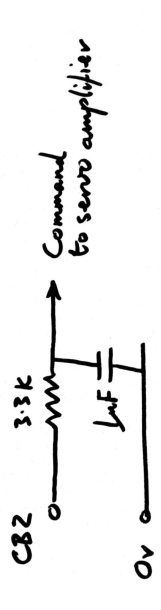

Figure 9.4 Smoothing to obtain analogue output

'wiper' pin of the potentiometer. With the circuit shown in **Figure 9.4**, the servomotor should follow the command potentiometer over its full range. This circuit uses a different dodge to increase stiffness, 'integral action'. In the short term, the output voltage will be about thirty times the error voltage — this may seem ample, but note that the position error to give full drive will be 1/30 of 270 degrees, and nine degrees can be a lot of movement in a servo. The integral term means that over a second or so the drive voltage will increase to double its value, winding down any error due to a standing motor load; after ten seconds, an error of one degree can result in full torque.

Analogue output from CB2

Now for that analogue output signal. It was mentioned in Chapter 4 that CB2 could be persuaded to act as a shift-register. If the control registers are set up correctly, any data byte planted in location &FE6A will be repeatedly output as a serial bit pattern on CB2. Now if &FE6A contains the value 1, the output pattern will be low for seven pulses and high for an eighth — the same is true for 2, 4, 8, 16, 32, 64 and 128. For value 3, the output will be low for six and high for two pulses, although 17 will give a better spacing. 73 is 01001001 in binary, and hence has three up and five down, and so on until with 255 the output is always high. By smoothing the output with a capacitor, nine output levels can be obtained: 0, 1/8, 1/4, 3/8, 1/2, 5/8, 3/4, 7/8 and 1 times the five volt supply. Nine levels are hardly enough; how can we get better resolution? Using our old friend the binary-rate-multiplier, we can increase the resolution to 256 values.

The output is now determined by an integer, $V\%$, say. The top 3 of the eight bits of $V\%$ low byte are used to select one of the eight 'patterns' 0, 1, 17, 73, 85, 182, 238 and 254 — a ninth pattern being 255. The bottom five bits of $V\%$ are masked off and added to a variable, SUM, say. Each time that SUM exceeds 31, the next higher pattern is used in the shift register, and 32 is subtracted from SUM. To get a smooth average, this operation must be repeated fifty or so times per second. To avoid the need for a loop in the program, this can be done with an 'interrupt'. The BASIC program goes its happy way, and every time a certain timer gives a pulse the computer's attention is diverted to an 'interrupt routine'. First this stores away the status and all necessary registers, then the processor leaps into the appropriate bit of machine code. After executing this, control must return to the tail-end of the interrupt routine which restores all the registers and status, carrying on with the original program as though nothing had happened.

The 'housekeeping' part of the interrupt routine is built into the computer's operating system, and all the links are set up by a simple *FX call. Now all you need to do, after planting and waking up the interrupt machine-code, is to save the required output value in variable V% and a corresponding value of voltage will magically appear on the capacitor and resistor attached to CB2. You have an analogue output.

To test the analogue output you can simply attach your test meter between CB2 and ground, on a voltage range of 5v or greater. The inertia of the needle is enough to smooth the output, and you do not even need the capacitor. Now enter and run the following program:

```
 10  DIM GAP% 100, PATTERN 10:REM ROOM FOR CODE
 20  FOR I = 0 TO 2 STEP 2
 30  P% = GAP%
 40  [OPT I
 50  .DTOA LDA 1112\1024 + 4*22 = V% ADDRESS
 60  LSR A
 70  LSR A
 80  LSR A
 90  LSR A
100  LSR A\SHIFT RIGHT TO GET TOP 3 BITS
110  TAX
120  LDA 1112\V%
130  AND #&1F\AND WITH 31
140  CLC  CLEAR CARRY
150  ADC SUM
160  CMP #&20
170  BMI NOMORE
180  INX
190  AND #&1F
200  .NOMORE STA SUM
210  LDA PATTERN,X
220  STA #&FE61A\PUT IN SHIFT REGISTER
230  RTS\GO AWAY
240  .SUM NOP
250  ]
260  NEXT I
270  FOR I = PATTERN TO PATTERN + 8:READ
A:?I = A:NEXT
280  DATA 0, 1, 17, 81, 85, 174, 238, 254, 255
300  ?&FE6B = 20:REM &14 MAKE CB2 S.REG., MAX SPEED
310  ?&220 = DTOA MOD 256: REM PLANT ADDRESS OF
320  ?&221 = DTOA DIV 256: REM DTOA ROUTINE
330  *FX 14,4
340   REM WAKE UP INTERRUPT AT SCREEN RATE
1000  FOR I = 0 TO 255
```

```
1010  V% = I: REM YES, THAT'S ALL IT TAKES
1020  A$ = INKEY$(20):REM BRIEF DELAY
1030  NEXT I
1040  GOTO 1000:REM OUTPUT ANOTHER RAMP
```

Driving radio-control servos

If you have ploughed through the preceding sections, you may feel that it is unfair to wait until now to tell you that there is another way to go about driving a servo. This method is a favourite of Alan Dibley, who uses it with devastating effect for building Micromice.

For radio-control, you can buy a servomotor off-the-shelf complete with drive amplifier. There is no need to worry about feedback, stability or tacho signals. The motor comes with a three-wire connection. Two are for power supply whilst the third is the command input.

Commands to the servo take the form of pulses every 20 milliseconds or so. The width of each pulse determines the commanded position, 1 millisecond giving full scale one way, varying to 2 milliseconds for full scale the other way. Once again we can use an interrupt to repeat the motor output, and we can again use the dodge of communicating with the interrupt routine by saving the value in V%. Now CB2 will give an output in the form of a train of pulses, and can be connected to the servo command input.

Radio-control servo program

```
 10  DIM GAP% 100: REM ROOM FOR CODE
 20  FOR I = 0 TO 2 STEP 2
 30  P% = GAP%
 40  [OPT I
 50  .DTOA LDX 1112\1024 + 4*22 = V% ADDRESS
 60  LDA # &E0\SET CB2 HIGH
 70  STA &FE6C
 80  INX\COVER CASE OF V% = 0
 90  .L1 DEX
100  BNE L1\COUNT V%
110  LDX #255\PREPARE FOR 1 MILLISEC
120  .L2 DEX\COUNT 1 MS
130  BNE L2
140  LDA #&C0\SET CB2 LOW
150  STA &FE6C
160  RTS\ALL DONE, GO HOME
```

```
250 ]
260 NEXT I
300 ?&220 = DTOA MOD 256: REM PLANT ADDRESS OF
310 ?&221 = DTOA DIV 256: REM DTOA ROUTINE
320 *FX 14,4
330 REM WAKE UP INTERRUPT AT SCREEN RATE
```

Note that the value loaded in line 110 may need to be changed — the servo may require a different pulsewidth. (Also I haven't had a chance to check out the exact timing value!)

Now the servo should respond to any value saved in variable V%, and you can use the following program as a simple test:

```
1000 FOR I = 0 TO 255
1010 V% = I: REM YES, THAT'S ALL IT TAKES
1020 A$ = INKEY$(20):REM BRIEF DELAY
1030 NEXT I
1040 GOTO 1000:REM OUTPUT ANOTHER RAMP
```

When you press BREAK after running the program, the computer will unravel the interrupt and leave all as normal.

D to A

```
 10 DIM GAP% 100,PATTERN 10 :REM ROOM FOR
CODE, TABLE
 20 FOR I=0 TO 2 STEP 2
 30     P%=GAP%
 40     [OPT I
 50     .DTOA LDA 1112 \ 1024+4*22=V% ADDRESS
 60     LSR A
 70     LSR A
 80     LSR A
 90     LSR A
100     LSR A \ SHIFT RIGHT TO GET TOP THREE
BITS
110     TAX
120     LDA 1112 \ V%
130     AND #&1F \ AND WITH 31
```

```
140    CLC         \ CLEAR CARRY
150    ADC SUM
160    CMP #&20
170    BMI NOMORE
180    INX
190    AND #&1F
200    .NOMORE STA SUM
210    LDA PATTERN,X
220    STA &FE6A \ PUT IN SHIFT REGISTER
230    RTS         \ GO AWAY
240    .SUM NOP
250    ]
260    NEXT I
270 FOR I=PATTERN TO PATTERN+8:READ A:?I=A:
NEXT I
280 DATA 0,1,17,81,85,174,238,254,255
300 ?&FE6B=20: REM &14 MAKE CB2 S.REG. MAX
SPEED
310 ?&220=DTOA MOD 256:REM PLANT ADDRESS OF
320 ?&221=DTOA DIV 256:REM DTOA ROUTINE
330 *FX 14,4
340 REM WAKE UP INTERRUPT AT SCREEN RATE
1000 FORI=0 TO 255
1010    V%=I:REM YES, THAT'S ALL IT TAKES
1020    A$=INKEY$(20):REM BRIEF DELAY
1030    NEXT I
1040 GOTO 1000:     REM OUTPUT ANOTHER RAMP
```

Radio Control Servo Drive

```
10 DIM GAP% 100 :REM ROOM FOR CODE
20 FOR I=0 TO 2 STEP 2
30    P%=GAP%
40    [OPT I
50    .DTOA LDA 1112 \ 1024+4*22=V% ADDRESS
60    LDA #&E0 \ SET CB2 HIGH
70    STA &FE6C
80    INX \ COVER CASE OF V%=0
90    .L1 DEX
100   BNE L1 \COUNT V%
110   LDX #255 \ PREPARE FOR 1 MS
```

```
120      .L2 DEX \ COUNT 1 MS
130      BNE L2
140      LDA #&C0 \ SET CB2 LO
150      STA &FE6C
160      RTS \ ALL DONE GO HOME
250      ]
260      NEXT I
300      ?&220=DTOA MOD 256:REM PLANT ADDRESS
OF
310      ?&221=DTOA DIV 256:REM DTOA ROUTINE
320      *FX 14,4
330      REM WAKE UP INTERRUPT AT SCREEN RATE
1000     FORI=0 TO 255
1010       V%=I:REM YES, THAT'S ALL IT TAKES
1020       A$=INKEY$(20):REM BRIEF DELAY
1030       NEXT I
1040     GOTO 1000:     REM OUTPUT ANOTHER RAMP
```

CHAPTER 10
Simple Robot Vision

Much of the work described in this chapter forms part of the research of Ali Hosseinmardi. Its publication here does not prejudice his claim to originality. The simplest vision system has been taken up by Upperdata Ltd, and is being marketed for the incredible price of £50. If you are industrious you can build your own 'eye' from scratch using the information here, but you might well take the lazy way out.

Provocative Instrumentation

The techniques of capturing analogue signals within the computer are many and various, and the computer is fast replacing the instrumentation recorder in process plants. Electrical signals which otherwise would have driven charts or pointers are dangled under the computer's nose, to be tasted at leisure. The computer is capable of better things than this.

The computer can perform experiments to obtain the data it needs, provoking the system to obtain a response — hence the term I have coined, 'Provocative Instrumentation'. The vision system is a prime example. A sighted man will analyse the signals which happen to arrive at his eye. The blind man must tap about with his stick, building up an image of his surroundings from the responses. This image may be less detailed than the sighted one, but it is much better than no image at all.

The Cyclops vision system equips the robot with just one single focussed photocell — the blind man's stick. This one point of vision is scanned about by the robot itself, enabling a picture to be built up. The slow way is to drive the robot in a raster scan, allowing the levels of grey to be written to the display screen to build up a conventional image. More interesting is the technique of allowing the robot to follow the edge of any contrasting feature, so that the image is analysed for shape even before it is completely input. One or two cunning techniques allow features to be followed even when they are grey-on-grey, and even when the unevenness of the illumination represents more contrast across the field of view than the feature itself.

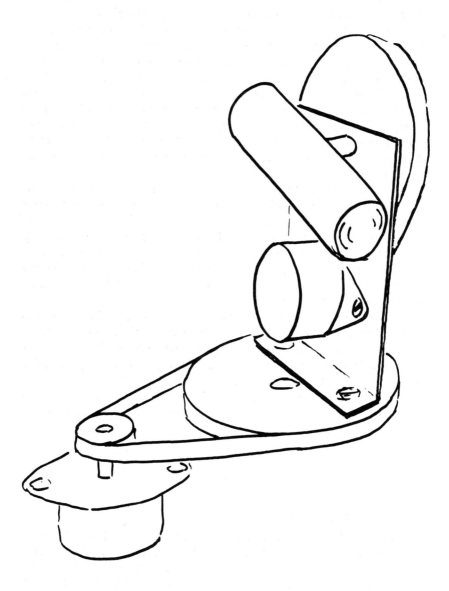

Figure 10.1   Mechanical mounting for eye

Making the vision system

As Mrs Beeton nearly said, 'First catch your robot'. You will need some means of deflecting the lens and photocell to scan the view. You can attach the 'eye' to the forearm of a ready-made robot such as the Armdroid, or you can relatively easily make up a special two-channel deflection system; it could end up looking much like the home-made joystick, with stepper motors in place of the potentiometers and the 'eye' in place of the joystick itself. Unfortunately the stepper motor steps are rather large, and twenty-four half-steps will cover a full ninety degrees. You will therefore need to find some way of gearing down the movement either with conventional gears or with a simple string and pulley system. If you overdo the gearing, you can always modify the software to give a number of steps of movement between sample points.

The eye is no more than a lens, a tube, a photocell (OP500 will do nicely) and a connecting cable. For humbler computers than the BBC micro, some extra circuitry is provided in the commercial version to give analogue-to-digital conversion, but for a machine with the foresight to provide a built-in converter this is hardly necesssary. One series resistor of about 2 kilohms is enough to allow the photocell current to develop a voltage which will satisfy the analogue port. For lower light levels a larger value of resistor can be used.

The lens should be 10 diopters or a little stronger — ie should have a focal length of 10 cm or less. A simple plastic magnifying glass could be ideal. If you are too fastidious to cut down a toilet roll tube to mount it in, a roll of paper can be held together with draughting tape. Once the photocell is fixed at the focal point and the tube is attached to the robot or scanner unit, little remains except the software. To check out your connections to the eye, and to make sure that the resistor is appropriate to the light level, you can key in and run the one-liner:

```
10 PRINT ADVAL(1):GOTO10
```

Two vision strategies

A quick and effective way to transfer an image to the screen is by means of a raster scan. The eye is scanned to and fro, moving steadily downwards, whilst a blob is written onto the screen at each point of an intensity corresponding to the photocell signal. In principle one scan line can be made from left to right, whilst the next is right to left. In practice backlash will cause alternate lines to be slightly shifted, and so a conventional raster is preferable. Now there are two nested 'FOR...NEXT' loops to command the motor movement. The light level is read at each point, and divided by a scale factor to give a result in a range, say, of 0 to 7. This

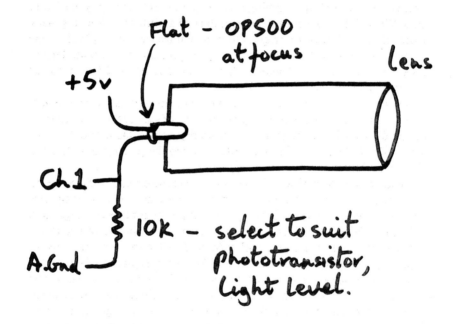

Figure 10.2   Connections of eye

number can be used to select a character from a string of increasingly dense symbols, which is then written to the corresponding screen position. Alternatively the value can be used to select the foreground colour, and a character written which is a solid block of colour. When displayed in black and white, the right choice of colours will appear as a grey-scale — you will have to use an array as a conversion table for deciding the colours, but that is easily dealt with.

An edge-following program is much more interesting. You can exploit the full resolution of the photocell, to detect edges which are light grey on dark. Let us start off by assuming that the picture is thoroughly black and white. We wish to move round the boundary of a white area, keeping black on our left and white on our right. Obviously since we can only look at one point at a time we will have to keep zig-zagging across the boundary to make sure that we do not lose it. A strategy that Ali and I have found effective is as follows.

Imagine that you have a compass drawn on a sheet of paper, with North and East marked. You are standing on an array of square tiles. The tile you are standing on is white, and you are facing North (as marked on the 'compass') along a row of more white tiles. On the paper are written the following rules:

1. If you are standing on a white square, rotate the compass 45 degrees to the west. Take a step 'Compass North', to the centre of the next square.
2. If you are standing on a black square, rotate the compass 45 degrees to the east. Take a step 'Compass East', to the centre of the next square.

If you follow the rules, you will turn half left and step forwards — diagonally. If this square is black, you will turn half right (now facing your original direction) and take a sideways step to the right. You are now just one square in front of your original position. If there is a row of black squares to the left of your row of white tiles, you will zig-zag forwards advancing one square each two moves. If your white squares come to an end, you will keep on turning half right until you again reach a white square, and so you will turn any corner of the boundary. It's hard to explain, but easy to program.

Now how can the strategy find an edge in a varying shade of grey? The technique involves setting up a local threshold level, midway between 'local-black' and 'local-white'. If the point you are now looking at is blacker than local-black, then local-black is immediately modified to that value. Similarly local-white is immediately changed if a whiter-than-white point is found. If the level lies somewhere between these values, then both values are allowed to edge inwards slightly, by assignments such as:

LOCALBLACK = LOCALBLACK +
(THRESHOLD – LOCALBLACK)/20

In this way the black/white decision is made about a threshold which can follow the variations of illumination across the image. Ali's experimental set up can trace the outline of a black letter, even when another sheet of paper is placed over the top of it — but the robot is apt to chase off after a crease in the paper.

By now you should have enough clues to write your own edge-following program, after you have tried out the raster program given below. It is hard to say when such a program is complete, since having captured a set of data-points representing the edge of the object, these need smoothing to remove the 'hem-stitch' pattern. They can then be processed to remove irrelevant points — straight lines can be sufficiently well represented by one point at each end, and a little cunning can reduce the outline of a K from several hundred points to fourteen. (Somehow the program seems unable to manage eleven).

The raster program

For any strategy, it is necessary to have a procedure for moving the robot. If you are using a complete Armdroid or such, then the procedure PROCMOVE of Chapter 8 can be wrapped up in a procedure PROCSHIFT(X,Y), where X and Y are the displacements to be made. In addition to lines 10000 to 11290 of Chapter 8, you will need:

```
11300  DEF PROCSHIFT(X,Y)
11310  TARGET(0) = TARGET(0) + X
11320  TARGET(1) = TARGET(1) + Y
11330 REM: THE CHANNEL NUMBERS ABOVE MAY BE
BOGUS — CHECK
11340  PROCMOVE
11350  ENDPROC
```

If you use this dodge, then in the routines which follow you will need to replace every PROCMOVE by a PROCSHIFT.

If instead of a ready-built robot you are using two stepper motors of your own, you can use the routine PROCMOVE(X,Y) of Chapter 7 (lines 10000 to 10640) just as it stands.

Since we might have two alternative attics to the program, let us keep the rest of the housekeeping downstairs, so that the program starts:

```
10  DIM CC(7) :REM COLOUR CONVERSION
20  FOR I = 0 TO 7:READ CC(I):NEXT
30  DATA 0,4,1,5,2,6,3,7
```

```
  40 REM BLACK,BLUE,RED,MAGENTA,GREEN,
CYAN,YELLOW,WHITE
  50 GOTO 10000
 100 LS = 65536/8:REM LIGHT SCALE
 110 VDU 23,255,255,255,255,255,255,255,255,255
 120 REM CHR$(255) IS NOW A SOLID BLOCK OF COLOUR
 130 MODE 2:REM 8 COLOURS + 8 FLASH, 32 ROWS, 20
COLUMNS
 140 XSCALE = 1:YSCALE = 1:REM ADJUST THE PICTURE
SHAPE

1000 CLS:CLG
1010 FOR ROW = 1 TO 32
1020 FOR COLUMN = 1TO20
1030 COLOUR (CC(ADVAL(1)/LS))
1040 PRINT CHR$(255);
1050 PROCMOVE(XSCALE,0)
1060 NEXT COLUMN
1070 PROCMOVE( – 20*XSCALE, – YSCALE)
1080 NEXT ROW
1090 PROCMOVE(0, – 32*YSCALE)
1100 A$ = INKEY$(0):IF A$ = ""THEN1100
1110 GOTO1000
```

This should be enough to transfer a view to the screen. If you are using a television set as a monitor, turning the colour right down will give you a grey-scale. If your set is black-and-white, you win hands down!

Of course that famous law will ensure that the photocell will start off pointing in the wrong direction. You will want to add:

```
 200 CLS:PRINT"SET EYE TO TOP LEFT OF SCENE"
 210 PRINT "MOVE RIGHT HOW MANY? ";:INPUT I
 220 PRINT "MOVE DOWN HOW MANY? ";:INPUT J
 230 PROCMOVE (XSCALE*I, – YSCALE*J)
 240 PRINT "OK?";:INPUT A$:IFA$< > "Y"THEN200
```

As soon as you are able to capture an image in the computer, a new world opens up in which you can try edge processing, image matching, two-dimensional filtering, and a variety of advanced techniques which are the subject of current research. The computer may fall short of 'real-time' analysis by a factor of hundreds in speed, and the 'pixel' resolution may not be marvellous, but the principles of any strategy should be within the capabilities of the machine.

Robot Vision

```
   10 DIM CC(7) :   REM COLOUR CONVERSION
   20 FOR I=0 TO 7:READ CC(I):PRINTCC(I):NEXT
   30 DATA 0,4,1,5,2,6,3,7
   40 REM BLACK,BLUE,RED,MAGENTA,GREEN,CYAN,
YELLOW,WHITE
   50 GOTO 10000
  100 LS=65536/8 : REM LIGHT SCALE
  110 VDU23,255,255,255,255,255,255,255,255,
255
  120 REM CHR$(255) IS NOW A SOLID BLOCK OF
COLOUR
  130 MODE 2:REM  8 COLOURS + 8 FLASH, 32 RO
WS 20 COLUMNS
  140 XSCALE=1:YSCALE=1:REM ADJUST THE PICTU
RE SHAPE
  150 VDU23,255,255,255,255,255,255,255,255,
255
  160 REM CHR$(255) IS NOW A SOLID BLOCK OF
COLOUR
  170 MODE 2:REM  8 COLOURS + 8 FLASH, 32 RO
WS 20 COLUMNS
  180 XSCALE=1:YSCALE=1:REM ADJUST THE PICTU
RE SHAPE
  200 CLS:PRINT "SET EYE TO TOP LEFT OF SCRE
EN"
  210 PRINT "MOVE RIGHT HOW MANY :";:INPUT I
  220 PRINT "MOVE DOWN  HOW MANY :";:INPUT J
  230 PROCSHIFT(XSCALE*I,-YSCALE*J)
  240 PRINT "O.K. ???";:INPUT A$
  250 IF A$<>"Y" THEN 200
 1000 CLS:CLG
 1010 FOR ROW=1 TO 32
 1020   FOR COLUMN=1 TO 20
 1030     COLOUR(CC(ADVAL(1)/LS))
 1040     PRINT CHR$ 255;
 1050     PROCSHIFT(XSCALE,0)
 1060   NEXT COLUMN
 1070   PROCSHIFT(-20*XSCALE,-YSCALE)
 1080   NEXT ROW
 1090 PROCSHIFT(0,-32*YSCALE)
 1100 A$=INKEY$(0):IF A$="" THEN 1100
```

```
 1110 GOTO 1000
10000 DIM DRIVE(7): REM VALUES WITH STROBE
 ALREADY HIGH
10010 FOR I=0 TO 7:READ J:DRIVE(I)=8*J+128:
 NEXT
10020 DATA 1,5,4,6,2,10,8,9
10030 MASK=127:?&FE60=128:?&FE62=255:REM MA
KE OUTPUTS
10100 DIM HERE(5),TARGET(5),RATE(5),WAY(5),
REG(5)
10110 FOR I=0 TO 5:HERE(I)=0:REG(I)=.5:PROC
ROBOT(I,0):NEXT
10120 SPEED=100
10300 NP=0:MP=20:REM MAX NUMBER OF POINTS -
CHANGE AD LIB
10310 DIM PNT(MP,5):REM MAKE ROOM FOR POINTS
10320 DIM COMMAND(12,5)
10330 FOR J=1 TO 12:REM FOR EACH COMMAND KEY
UDLRFBWVTYOC
10340    FOR I=0 TO 5:READ COMMAND(J,I):NEXT:
NEXT
10350 DATA   0, 1, 0, 0, 0, 0 :REM U
10360 DATA   0,-1, 0, 0, 0, 0 :REM D
10370 DATA   1, 0, 0, 0, 0, 0 :REM L
10380 DATA  -1, 0, 0, 0, 0, 0 :REM R
10390 DATA   0, 0, 1, 0, 0, 0 :REM F
10400 DATA   0, 0,-1, 0, 0, 0 :REM B
10410 DATA   0, 0, 0,-1, 1, 0 :REM W
10420 DATA   0, 0, 0, 1,-1, 0 :REM V
10430 DATA   0, 0, 0, 1, 1, 0 :REM T
10440 DATA   0, 0, 0,-1,-1, 0 :REM Y
10450 DATA   0, 0, 0, 0, 0, 1 :REM O
10460 DATA   0, 0, 0, 0, 0,-1 :REM C
10470 REM DATA ABOVE IS BOGUS !!!
10480 REM SORT OUT CHANNELS YOURSELF
10900   GOTO 100:REM END OF HOUSE KEEPING
11040 DEF PROCROBOT(CHANNEL,VLUE)
11050 X=DRIVE(VLUE AND 7)+CHANNEL
11060 ?&FE60=X
11070 ?&FE60=X AND MASK
11080 ?&FE60=X
11090 ENDPROC
11120 DEF PROCMOVE: REM MOVE FROM HERE TO
TARGET
```

113

```
11130 RMAX=0:FORI=0TO5
11140    RATE(I)=ABS(TARGET(I)-HERE(I)):REM
  DISTANCE AND
11150    WAY(I)=SGN(TARGET(I)-HERE(I)):REM DI
RECTION EACH AXIS
11160    IF RATE(I)>RMAX THEN RMAX=RATE(I):RE
M FIND MAX DISTANCE
11170    NEXT:IF RMAX=0 THEN ENDPROC:   REM NO
  MOVE
11180 FORI=0TO5
11190    RATE(I)=RATE(I)/RMAX:NEXT:REM RATE
  NOW IN RANGE 0 TO 1
11200 FOR R=1 TO RMAX:REM NOW WE ARE READY
  TO MOVE
11210    FOR CHAN=0TO5
11220      REG(CHAN)=REG(CHAN)+RATE(CHAN)
11230      IF REG(CHAN)<1 THEN 11260
11240      REG(CHAN)=REG(CHAN)-1:HERE(CHAN)=
HERE(CHAN)+WAY(CHAN)
11250      PROCROBOT(CHAN,HERE(CHAN))
11260      NEXT CHAN
11270    FOR I=0 TO 1000 STEP SPEED:NEXT:REM
  DELAY
11280    NEXTR
11290 ENDPROC :REM NOW HERE=TARGET
11300 DEF PROCSHIFT(X,Y)
11310 TARGET(0)=TARGET(0)+X
11320 TARGET(1)=TARGET(1)+Y
11330 REM CHANNEL NUMBERS ABOVE MAY BE BOGU
S, CHECK THEM
11340 PROCMOVE
11350 ENDPROC
```

CHAPTER 11
Whatever Next?

It has taken a long time for the great computer manufacturers to acknowledge the existence of the micro. Despite their efforts at ignoring it, it wouldn't go away. At first, low-cost microcomputer systems were little more than toys, so obviously handicapped by their eight-bit inferiority that they couldn't ever threaten the mainframe — or could they? Their accessibility attracted many people to software writing, some of whom would cringe at the tag 'computer scientist', and before long a wealth of ingenious packages were hitting the market, ranging from word processors to spreadsheet calculators, from payrolls to catering analysis. As the supply of peripherals moved upmarket in performance and downmarket in price, it became obvious that the micro was no mere lightweight but was set to become the cornerstone of commerce — as shown by no less than five commercials per night on Thames TV. When sixteen-bit chips appeared, the giants started to stir — although their software was mainly based on transcriptions of eight-bit routines and seldom gave any speed advantage. Now the mainframe manufacturers are scrambling to integrate micros into their marketing strategies.

The same story is starting to unfold for robots.

Robot evolution

Production engineers have long been familiar with Numerically Controlled machine tools. Controlled by barbaric means such as punched paper tape, these are identical in concept with the rest of the industrial robots. Instructions programmed once are repeated to produce a stream of identical products. Change the instructions, and the same expensive machine tool can produce a different product — the start of a Flexible Manufacturing System. Only when the anthropomorphic robot 'arm' appeared did the term 'robot' gain general acceptance for this type of automation, a name carried by the IBM robot which is more like the arrangement of a milling machine than like a human arm. Industrial robots in this league carry price tags of tens of thousands of pounds, and a vision system may cost several times more.

Then the educational robots appeared on the scene. A few hundred pounds could buy a rather tinny device, admittedly resembling a toy version of the business end of a JCB. This could be connected to almost any High Street microcomputer to be programmed in a way resembling its larger cousin. Its lifting power was practically zero and its speed was not remarkable, but robots were no longer the exclusive property of major industries. Even to these humble devices sensors could be added and linked with programs which leaned towards intelligence. As small firms (and some large institutions) experimented with the possibilities of cheap automation, it became clear that a demand was growing for the robot which could combine relative cheapness with a usable performance. Just as the microcomputer grew to fill its market place, so the microrobot is stretching its muscles to find industrial application.

With the microcomputer has grown a generation of youngsters made familiar in school and at home with micro programming. Some have made fortunes as entrepreneurs, others have found sadly that computer programming can be as lowly paid as shorthand-typing. As micros throughout schools and homes become equipped with robots, so another generation will take industrial automation in its stride. Every back-street workshop will be able to afford a robot or two, and the expertise to set them up will likewise not be exclusive. For a while, however, experience with robots will be a highly prized commodity, and I hope that this book will give you a start.

Robot intelligence

The definition of a robot can be broadened to embrace any machine which is a 'robotnik' — a worker. It is not hard to include automatic washing machines and dish-washers, which after all measure such variables as water level and temperature and apply programmed control accordingly. Although a 'micromouse' does little work, it is surely a robot. The mice which have struggled to the centre of the Euromicro 'Euromouse' maze have used sensors and actuators with a large amount of intelligence — if only by proxy from their designers. Industrial robots too are starting to depart from the 'do just as I tell you' image, and apply correction and adaptation to the way in which they perform their tasks, in order to achieve a more generally specified goal. (With some difficulty I suppress an urge to go into the details of the 'Craftsman Robot' project, for which my group are receiving support from the SERC).

The major maze-solving algorithm was established by Nick Smith, first Euromouse champion in 1980. It involved allocating numbers to the squares, starting from zero at the centre. Any square accessible from the centre was numbered one, any square accessible from a one-square was numbered two, and so on. As new walls were found, links to lower-numbered squares were broken, and the values 'floated up'. The best way to the centre was found by following the numbers downwards —

until a new wall was met. A pedant would insist on calling the technique 'recursive dynamic programming'. Micromice then started to win through agility and especially reliability. David Woodfield's 'Thumper' still performs almost impeccably two years after its 1981 victory. Alan Dibley introduced the concept of the 'economy mouse'. Cutting the keyboard off the cheapest available micro, he mounts it on a plywood or balsa frame controlled by commercial model aircraft servos. Using the technique mentioned in Chapter 9, he achieves a considerable measure of success — although not enough of late to defeat the Finnish champions. Of particular significance is the appearance in the contest of school teams, even making the pilgrimage to Madrid. Their mice may have much room for improvement, but the pattern has been set. A school team might even become the Copenhagen champions, to go on to an expenses-paid trip to compete in Japan's own contest.

Robot ping-pong

What contest can try the mettle of the robot professionals? I have proposed a contest of robot ping-pong, and have already received several dozen serious enquiries from potential contestants (or should I say potential designers). The date for the first match has been set for 1986, although I strongly suspect that this will be brought forward to 1985. The contest is not as far-fetched as it may first appear. The table is a mere half-metre wide, and is two metres long. Half-metre square frames at each end and above the net restrict the allowable movement of the ball, and reduce the area which the robots must be able to reach. The net is a quarter metre high, and this in turn makes a slam a recipe for losing a point. Simulations show that in order to make a return difficult, a robot must deliver the ball with great precision.

The serve is handled by the table itself. The ball starts at rest suspended from the centre frame above the net. When both robot vision systems have locked onto it, a nearly transparent 'fly swat' pats the ball towards the robot 'on serve'. The ball bounces once before emerging from the 'playing frame', and the robot must return it to bounce once before emerging from the opponent's playing frame. And so the game goes on.

A few calculations show that the dexterity required is not enormous. A good X-Y plotter mounted close to the playing frame could form most of the hardware. The bat can be held by its centre by a glorified pen-lift, which is armed by a small motor and fired as the ball approaches the bat. Bat tilt can be added, or the same effect can be gained from a curved bat surface and precise placing. The number of alternative designs is at least as big as the variety of micromice, and there is no reason to suppose that entries will

117

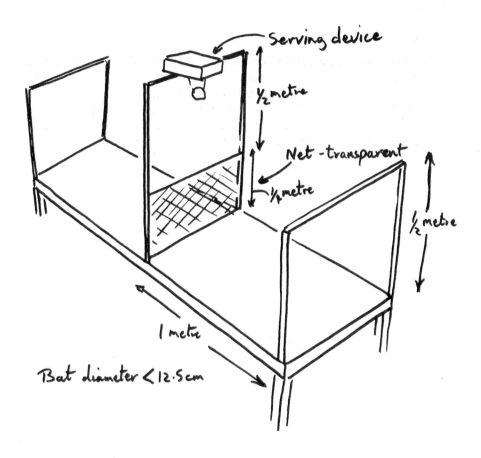

Serving device

½ metre

Net -transparent

½ metre

½ metre

1 metre

Bat diameter < 12.5 cm

Figure 11.1   Table for robot ping-pong

be confined to the 'professionals'. What is clear is that success will be earned by a combination of agile optical tracking and ingenious strategic play.

Interest in the competition is already becoming international. From the interest shown by the Japanese delegates to the Madrid Euromicro, they may be as quick to adopt robot ping-pong as they were to adopt Euromouse.

In conclusion

Microprocessors and robots may do all the pundits claim, in establishing a new industrial revolution. Manufactured goods will probably continue to slide in price, and only a nation of Luddites would continue to rely on monotonous assembly-line work as the basis of the national economy. You may be able to hasten the revolution a little; it would be hard to delay it. But whatever economic significance robots may have, they are enormous fun.

Other titles from Sunshine

SPECTRUM BOOKS

Spectrum Adventures
A guide to playing and writing adventures
Tony Bridge & Roy Carnell   £5.95
ISBN 0 946408 07 6

ZX Spectrum Astronomy
Maurice Gavin   £6.95
ISBN 0 946408 24 6

Spectrum Machine Code Applications
David Laine   £6.95
ISBN 0 946408 17 3

The Working Spectrum
David Lawrence   £5.95
ISBN 0 946408 00 9

Master your ZX Microdrive
Andrew Pennell   £6.95
ISBN 0 946408 19 X

COMMODORE 64 BOOKS

Graphic Art for the Commodore 64
Boris Allan   £5.95
ISBN 0 946408 15 7

Mathematics on the Commodore 54
Czes Kosniowski   £5.95
ISBN 0 946408 14 9

Commodore 64 Adventures
Mike Grace   £5.95
ISBN 0 946408 11 4

Business Applications for the Commodore 64
James Hall   £5.95
ISBN 0 946408 12 2

The Working Commodre 64
David Lawrence   £5.95
ISBN 0 946408 02 5

Commodore 64 Machine Code Master
David Lawrence & Mark England   £6.95
ISBN 0 946408 05 X

ELECTRON BOOKS

Graphic Art for the Electron
Boris Allan   **£5.95**
ISBN 0 946408 20 3

Programming for Education on the Electron Computer
John Scriven & Parick Hall   **£5.95**
ISBN 0 946408 21 1

BBC COMPUTER BOOKS

Functional Forth for the BBC computer
Boris Allan   **£5.95**
ISBN 0 946408 04 1

Graphic Art for the BBC Computer
Boris Allan   **£5.95**
ISBN 0 946408 08 4

Programming for Education on the BBC computer
John Scriven & Parick Hall   **£5.95**
ISBN 0 946408 10 6

DRAGON BOOKS

Advanced Sound & Graphics for the Dragon
Keith & Steven Brain   **£5.95**
ISBN 0 946408 06 8

Dragon 32 Games Master
Keith & Steven Brain   **£5.95**
ISBN 0 946408 03 3

The Working Dragon
David Lawrence   **£5.95**
ISBN 0 946408 01 7

The Dragon Trainer
A handbook for beginners
Boris Lloyd   **£5.95**
ISBN 0 946408 09 2

ATARI BOOKS

Writing Strategy Games on your Atari Computer
John White   **£5.95**
ISBN 0 946408 22 X

Sunshine also publishes

POPULAR COMPUTING WEEKLY

The first weekly magazine for home computer users. Each copy contains Top 10 charts of the best-selling software and books and up-to-the-minute details of the latest games. Other features in the magazine include regular hardware and software reviews, programming hints, computer swap, adventure corner and pages of listings for the Spectrum, Dragon, BBC, VIC 20 and 64, ZX 81 and other popular micros. Only 35p a week, a year's subscription costs £19.95 (£9.98 for six months) in the UK and £37.40 (£18.70 for six months) overseas.

DRAGON USER

The monthly magazine for all users of Dragon microcomputers. Each issue contains reviews of software and peripherals, programming advice for beginners and advanced users, program listings, a technical advisory service and all the latest news related to the Dragon. A year's subscription (12 issues) costs £8.00 in the UK and £14.00 overseas.

MICRO ADVENTURER

The monthly magazine for everyone interested in Adventure games, war gaming and simulation/role-playing games. Includes reviews of all the latest software, lists of all the software available and programming advice. A year's subscription (12 issues) costs £10 in the UK and £16 overseas.

COMMODORE HORIZONS

The monthly magazine for all users of Commodore computers. Each issue contains reviews of software and peripherals, programming advice for beginners and advanced users, program listings, a technical advisory service and all the latest news. A year's subscription costs £10 in the UK and £16 overseas.

For further information contact:
Sunshine
12–13 Little Newport Street
London WC2R 3LD
01-437 4343

Printed in England by Commercial Colour Press, London E7.

NOTES

NOTES

NOTES

NOTES

NOTES